W9-BLB-735

LIFE NATURE LIBRARY.

THE LAND AND WILDLIFE OF
EURASIA

TIME LIFE BOOKS ®

LIFE NATURE LIBRARY

THE LAND AND WILDLIFE OF

EURASIA

by François Bourlière
and The Editors of LIFE

TIME INCORPORATED
NEW YORK

About the Author

François Bourlière was born in Roanne, France, in 1913, took a degree in medicine and is presently a professor at the medical faculty of the University of Paris. However, he is far more than a physician and teacher. For years he has been interested in many aspects of the natural world: he is an outstanding mammalogist and is internationally known for his researches in vertebrate ecology. He has done extensive field work not only in his native Europe, but also in tropical Africa, Southeast Asia and the Caribbean region. His studies of animals have led him into human ecology and from there into the problems of aging in human beings. His investigations in this specialized field are conducted at the Claude Bernard Gerontological Center in Paris, a unique research institution of which he is the scientific director. Despite these many preoccupations, Dr. Bourlière has found the time to write two books, *The Natural History of Mammals* (1954, revised edition 1964) and *Mammals of the World* (1955), both of which are standard works in English as well as French. He founded and now edits the French quarterly journal of applied ecology, *La Terre et la Vie*, and is chairman of the International Union for Conservation of Nature and Natural Resources. He holds a corresponding membership awarded by The American Museum of Natural History, and a corresponding fellowship awarded by the American Ornithologists Union. Married and the father of three children, he lives in Paris.

ON THE COVER: Morning light hits the peaks overlooking a pass in the Hindu Kush. This range, in Afghanistan, forms the southwest portion of Eurasia's great mountain system, the world's loftiest.

Contents

TIME-LIFE BOOKS

EDITOR
Maitland A. Edey
EXECUTIVE EDITOR
Jerry Korn
TEXT DIRECTOR   ART DIRECTOR
Martin Mann   Sheldon Cotler
CHIEF OF RESEARCH
Beatrice T. Dobie
PICTURE EDITOR
Robert G. Mason
Assistant Text Directors:
Harold C. Field, Ogden Tanner
Assistant Art Director: Arnold C. Holeywell
Assistant Chief of Research: Martha Turner

•

PUBLISHER
Rhett Austell
General Manager: Joseph C. Hazen Jr.
Planning Director: John P. Sousa III
Circulation Director: Joan D. Manley
Marketing Director: Carter Smith
Business Manager: John D. McSweeney
Publishing Board: Nicholas Benton, Louis Bronzo,
James Wendell Forbes

LIFE MAGAZINE

EDITOR: Edward K. Thompson
MANAGING EDITOR: George P. Hunt
PUBLISHER: Jerome S. Hardy

LIFE NATURE LIBRARY

EDITOR: Maitland A. Edey
Associate Editor: Percy Knauth
Assistant to the Editor: John Paul Porter
Designer: Paul Jensen
Staff Writers: Dale Brown, Mary Louise Grossman
Chief Researcher: Martha Turner
Researchers: Gerald A. Bair, Doris Bry, Eleanor Feltser,
Nancy J. Jacobsen, LeClair G. Lambert, Paula Norworth,
Carol Phillippe, Marjorie M. Pickens, Susan Rayfield,
Roxanna Sayre, Nancy Shuker, John von Hartz

EDITORIAL PRODUCTION
Color Director: Robert L. Young
Copy Staff: Marian Gordon Goldman, Joan Chambers,
Florence Keith
Picture Department: Dolores A. Littles, Barbara Sullivan
Art Assistants: James D. Smith, Mark A. Binn,
John Newcomb

The text for this book was written by François Bourlière, the picture essays by the editorial staff. The following individuals and departments of Time Inc. were helpful in producing the book: LIFE staff photographers Larry Burrows, Ralph Crane, Dmitri Kessel and Ralph Morse; LIFE contributing photographer Howard Sochurek; the Chief of the LIFE Picture Library, Doris O'Neil; the Chief of the TIME-LIFE News Service, Richard M. Clurman; and the Chief of the Bureau of Editorial Reference, Peter Draz.

Introduction

ONE can scarcely imagine a task more difficult than that accomplished by the author of this book. In a volume of limited size, he has undertaken to synthesize and compress subject matter of virtually unlimited scope. In the first instance, he deals with an immense physical area, Eurasia, the largest integrated land mass on earth, one that runs to extremes in the variety of its land forms, its climates and the living things, both animals and plants, that exist upon it. In addition to viewing this subject in the contemporary period, he gives recognition to the effects of vast time spaces extending from the Cambrian age of some 500 million years ago to the present day. Through the inclusion of the evolutionary story that has resulted in the present physical constitution of Eurasia, there is revealed the drama of the genesis and metamorphosis of that vast continent. All this has been accomplished with high competence, and the result is a book of exceptional interest and value—enhanced by the fine illustrations that fill its pages.

It has required a man of François Bourlière's extensive knowledge and experience to deal with the subject in this manner. His professional qualifications, ranging from that of physician to mammalogist, are supplemented by his familiarity with geology and botany, and enriched by his awareness of the extent to which human actions affect the natural world. The significance of this human-earth relationship is at last being widely recognized, especially because of the explosive increase in human populations.

Within the story of evolutionary forces over vast reaches of time, it is of particular interest to note the great changes that have occurred in both animal and plant life in relatively recent times, namely, during the series of ice ages of the last several hundred thousand years. These changes reveal the remarkable capacity for rapid movement by both animals and plants when impelled by major climatic change, or, alternately, the extinction of numerous species simply because physical barriers on the earth's surface prevented migrations from an intolerable to a favorable climatic environment.

The author rightly concerns himself not only with the results of man's misuse of the land within recent history, but also with the present acute crisis brought about by him in the survival of wildlife. In this latter regard, however, he has some encouraging words to say about the restoration of the European elk and the saiga antelope, as well as the initial, limited success being gained in the protection of the European wisent and the ibex. It is only too evident that the establishment of national parks and similar reserves for the living wild heritages of the past, whether animal or plant, is today an imperative need throughout the world.

The book is the first of a series of six that will introduce the major land areas of this earth. May they all prove as valuable and interesting.

FAIRFIELD OSBORN
President, New York Zoological Society

ANIMALS OF ANCIENT EURASIA LEAP IN MUTED LIFE ACROSS THE WALLS OF LASCAUX, FRANCE'S FAMOUS PREHISTORIC CAVE. THIS MURAL WAS

1 A Continent's Turbulent Past

PAINTED SOME 170 CENTURIES AGO AND SHOWS TWO BIG AUROCHS, EXTINCT FOR THREE CENTURIES, ALONG WITH SOME WILD HORSES AND DEER

THE story of Eurasia is a far more intriguing and enlightening tale than anyone interested in the earth's history might at first assume. We know this continent today as a vast, brooding, often dramatic land mass that reaches from Europe's teeming seaports to the icy wastes of the Bering Strait, a distance spanning half the circumference of the globe. We look at it and it appears as a single unit, a sweep of land bounded by the Atlantic and Arctic Oceans, the Mediterranean Sea, the tremendous Himalayas and the lonely reaches of the North Pacific—and simply from its mass it seems that it must always have been so. And yet, only the briefest look at what Eurasia encompasses today shows that this is not only the largest of continents, but also one of the most varied, in its landscape, its climate, its flora and its fauna; and these are only the visible remnants of a past which, as we reconstruct it, emerges as a giant jigsaw puzzle of our planet's turbulent evolution.

Eurasia today has a sample of every kind of climate, from tropical to Arctic, and with it nearly every kind of vegetation. It has the world's densest populations and some of its most primeval wildernesses. It boasts the highest mountains, in the Himalayas, and the deepest lake, in Lake Baikal.* Much of man's earliest history, as well as the history of plants and animals long before man, has been reconstructed from its famous fossils; and man himself, creating brilliant civilizations there, spread out from his Eurasian base to conquer all the rest of the globe. Eurasia reaches across to most of the earth's other major land masses, extending a finger toward the Americas at the Bering Strait, a bridge to Australasia via the Indonesian archipelago, and a broad highway down to Africa. To historians it is the parent continent of civilization. But it is also a great paradox: its size and variety suggest that it should be the parent continent in other ways also, but it is not. Geologically speaking, it can claim no such parenthood at all—it was formed only after a number of false starts as a composite of several land masses which did not join together for a long, long time.

THE PALEARCTIC ZONE

The area shown in color on this map is the Palearctic zone—the subject of this book. It includes that part of Europe and Asia that lies north of a dotted line running along the Himalayas, across Arabia and up through the Red Sea to the Mediterranean. Also included in the Palearctic zone is a narrow strip of coastal North Africa. The region south of it is striped to denote that there is disagreement among experts as to whether or not it should be included in the Palearctic.

THE origins of this largest of continents go back to the very dawn of our planet, but the continent-to-be bore no resemblance whatever to the land mass we know now. Basically, it was represented by an archipelago of giant islands, or shields, of Precambrian rock, rising above the surface of the vast seas which then covered much of our world. Essentially, these islands were five in number: the Scandinavian shield in the northwest; the Siberian shield, largest of all, in the north; the Chinese shield in the east; the Thailand-Cambodian in the southeast; and the Indian shield in the south.

The seas above which these great islands rose in these earliest days of the earth's formation have long since disappeared, but two of them, the Tethys and the Uralian, lasted for so long that they played a decisive role in the history of Old World flora and fauna. The Tethys was the southern of these two enormous bodies of water: it lay between the Scandinavian, Siberian and Chinese shields in the north and the Indian and African shields in the south. Thus it reached from the Alps and the Mediterranean basin all the way to the Timor Sea in the Indonesian archipelago, covering the entire width of southern Asia. Turkey, Iran, the mountain systems of the Middle East, the Himalayas, Yunnan and Vietnam—all lay submerged beneath the waters of what was, in fact, a tropical ocean. And though its shorelines changed during the more than 560 million years of its existence, and temporary isthmuses appeared and disappeared, the Tethys persisted more or less from the Precambrian period up to the middle of the Cenozoic era. The Mediterranean today is a relic of it, a remaining puddle, so to speak, of a vastly greater Mediterranean ocean.

Not until Oligocene times, some 36 million years ago, did the Tethys at last begin to dry up, eventually leaving behind it some of the familiar contours of the lands we know today. Great upheavals of the earth's crust gave birth to the Alps and the Himalayas, isolated its entire central area, and the two ends of this enormous sea became separated by thousands of miles of emerged land. But the common parentage of the Mediterranean and the seas around Japan is still evident in the great resemblance of the fishes found in these widely

*This and other place names will be found on a map on pages 192 and 193.

separated waters: these two areas have 79 genera and even some species in common. By contrast, the Mediterranean and the Red seas, separated by only a hundred miles or so of land, have quite different fishes, and it was not until the Suez Canal was cut in 1869 that they began to mingle.

The second and more northern sea, the Uralian, likewise went back to very early times. It ran north from the Tethys to what is now the Arctic Ocean and it separated the Siberian from the Scandinavian shield. In this general form it persisted through various changing shorelines from the beginning of the Paleozoic era for about 360 million years down to the late Permian. At that point, about 240 million years ago, what were to be the Ural mountains began to emerge. There was a general raising of land which lifted the level of the continent-to-be above the waves, giving Eurasia its first shape. The Uralian Sea disappeared—but only for a while. Succeeding upheavals and subsidences of the continental crust created new seas separating east from west more than once before the continent was again reunited at the end of Oligocene times. Thus Eurasia, as we know it today, has existed only for about 25 million years.

Of course, the contours of Eurasia's five principal island "foundation stones" did not remain unchanged during these hundreds of millions of years. What we have just said about the advances and retreats of the Uralian Sea tells us that their outlines must have varied considerably in the course of time. For example, from the Jurassic period onward, the Siberian shield, accumulating sediment on its flanks, expanded slowly but continuously to the southeast and ended up by joining with the Chinese shield to form an enormous land mass stretching from the Arctic to the equator. This coalescing process, in varying degrees of scope and permanence, went on among the other shields as well, and there were also temporary attachments to other continents.

One of these, which appeared at various stages of Eurasia's evolution and sometimes persisted for prolonged periods before it became submerged again, was an isthmus that spanned what is now roughly the Bering Strait, joining the Siberian shield to North America. The impassable barrier of the Uralian Sea in those times still isolated the far eastern areas from Europe—and Europe, on its part, shows some evidence of having been for a long time attached to the Greenland and Canadian shields. Thus there may have existed a North Atlantic continent; and while it was there, animals migrating from the Siberian shield to Europe had to travel eastward, not westward as today, first crossing the Bering isthmus and then traversing North America, finally entering Europe across what is now the bed of the Atlantic Ocean.

W HAT of the climate and of the evolution of life during the immensely long period in which Eurasia grew to be a continent? For much of this time the weather was almost uniformly warm and humid. Somewhere in the seas and shallows surrounding the primordial continental islands living matter appeared. In the Cambrian period, vegetation was rudimentary. This we know from traces of spores which have been discovered in rocks in Scandinavia, eastern Siberia, Kashmir and Punjab. Later, coral reefs appeared in all latitudes. In the warm seas large mollusks very similar to the present-day *Nautilus* were abundant. The first known terrestrial invertebrates, too, made their appearance on the emerged lands and left their mark in the form of scorpion fossils preserved in upper Silurian rocks in Scotland and in Gotland off the Swedish coast.

The warm weather continued for millennium after millennium, and by the start of the Devonian period, 400 million years ago, vegetation was luxuriant

HOW EURASIA GREW

PRECAMBRIAN

The original building blocks that eventually became the Eurasian continent were already in existence 600 million years ago. Clockwise from the left, they are: the Scandinavian, the Siberian, the Chinese, the Thailand-Cambodian and the Indian shields. The east-west watery space between was the Tethys Sea.

SILURIAN

Nearly 200 million years later the shields were still there, although they had been built out along their edges by accretions of marine sediment. Unlike the later rock additions, the Precambrian shields have risen and fallen little with time and even today they have almost no sedimentary layers lying on top of them

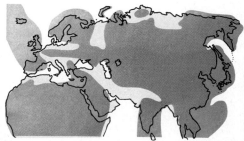

CRETACEOUS

By the Cretaceous, 150 million years ago, Eurasia had begun to look somewhat as it does today, though still cut up by extensive inland seas. Something resembling the Mediterranean existed, but with a sea connection to the east. An ocean arm still penetrated north of India, where the Himalayas would later rise.

as far north as Spitsbergen. Giant ferns and gymnosperms grew there, sheltering scorpions, myriapods and spiders. In the brackish waters and in the lagoons crawled huge horseshoe crabs, some of them six feet in length. The first fishes had put in their appearance, ostracoderms and lungfish. And in the late Devonian, there appeared the first amphibious vertebrates, the labyrinthodonts, whose caudal fin, spine and part of the skull remained fishlike, while the rest of the skull and the four limbs showed amphibian developments. By the Carboniferous period, the emerged lands nourished club mosses 120 feet high, 30-foot horsetails, conifers and an extreme abundance of plants with fernlike leaves, some of them true ferns, others seed ferns. Insects had increased in size and number, the largest being giant dragonflies with a wingspread over two feet. Fresh waters swarmed with clams and fish. Amphibians were becoming more numerous, and the first true reptiles appeared.

THE warm and humid climate of these times of burgeoning evolution persisted for 320 million years all told, down into the Permian period, but in places there were signs of aridity. By the beginning of the next era, the Mesozoic, the emerged lands were a veritable desert, interspersed, it seems, with closed basins similar to the shotts—the shallow salt lakes of North Africa today—and slow-running rivers along whose banks life was concentrated, somewhat in the manner of the modern Nile. Characteristic of the time was the "gallery forest" in the area of the Vosges mountains of France near the German border, where plants reminiscent of modern horsetails and ferns mingled with gymnosperms similar to the tall monkey puzzle trees of today. Hordes of insects, mostly beetles and cockroaches, but also May flies and enormous dragonflies, swarmed on the ground or skimmed the waters. Scorpions were plentiful and small horseshoe crabs dragged themselves along river banks, while crustaceans and fishes were at home in the warm waters.

Among land vertebrates, this was the Age of Reptiles. Turtles and armored reptiles were prevalent, among them crocodilelike creatures such as *Aëtosaurus*, an entire family of which, buried in a sandstorm, has been found in the Keuper beds near Stuttgart in Germany. There were also various kinds of lizardlike reptiles known as protorosaurs, one of which, living in central Europe, had a disproportionately long neck. Large predators were represented in the main by the phytosaurs, a group of reptiles very similar to modern crocodiles, but much larger, some of them up to 20 feet long. Beside these giants, the first dinosaurs in Europe and western China were modest in size. No larger than a modern monitor lizard, they were probably already competing with the many mammal-like reptiles which lived in Eurasia throughout the Triassic period, some already approaching the status of warm-blooded animals.

Imperceptibly the Triassic age gave way to the Jurassic. At least 420 million years had passed since the emergence of the continent's original island shields, and still the bulk of what would be Eurasia continued to lie beneath the warm and shallow seas. The south of Europe lay under the Tethys, which by now had formed itself into a series of basins connected by broad straits. Europe was, in effect, nothing but a group of islands. The land bridge to Greenland had disappeared, and a new Uralian Sea reunited the Tethys with the Arctic Ocean. The European archipelago was for a long time cut off from Asia as well as from America. In the Cerin Channel in east central France, a modern traveler would have believed himself to be on the Great Barrier Reef of Australia. Behind the sheltering reef, placid channels were dotted with low-lying coral

THE CLIMATE OF THE PAST

MEAN
TEMPERATURE
(F.)

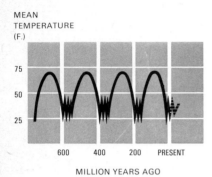

Although the farther back one goes in time the shakier the evidence becomes, it is still possible to construct a graph of probable temperate-zone temperatures for the past 600 million years through geological studies. What causes the strange 200-million-year cycles of hot and cold weather is still completely unknown to science, although there are numerous theories, some based on changes in solar radiation, others on the presence of dust in space or on shifts of the earth's axis. Whatever the cause, it is clear that we are in a cold period now. It is certain to get much warmer; the question is when.

islands on which dense mangroves grew. In these shallow waters a fine coral dust settled continuously, forming a deposit known today as lithographic limestone because of its use by mankind in printing and lithography. Midday temperatures rose so high that many fish died of suffocation: their skeletons have been found, admirably fossilized with their mouths wide open.

It was at this time that the famous lithographic limestones of the atolls and lagoons of Solnhofen in Germany were deposited. Animals venturing onto this extremely soft ground, whether it was covered with water or not, were often sucked in as by quicksand. The remarkable state of preservation of some of the fossils permits an exact reconstruction of all the little dramas acted out on these antique shores. Here we find a serpent star fossilized in the act of crawling; there an insect lies with spread wings, the fossil rock still showing the funnel-like marks left as it beat them in a vain effort to escape. Here again is a tiny lizardlike creature, closely resembling the modern tuataras of New Zealand. The story is clear: it became mired in the limestone mud, succeeded at first in freeing itself, but then, falling on its side, sank back too deeply to move again.

On the emerged lands the vegetation had now changed markedly, and the archaic plants which had survived the Triassic period were now replaced by an increasing number of new forms, certain of which persist to this day: cycads and conifers like the *Ginkgo* and *Metasequoia*. This flora was wholly cosmopolitan, with the same plants appearing from Spitsbergen to Siberia and from Japan to India. The land fauna had also undergone considerable changes. Dinosaurs, no longer small and inconspicuous, were now the dominant land vertebrates. Gigantic 30-ton *Brontosaurus* and other sauropods wallowed in the marshes and rivers, sometimes coming ashore to feed. The somewhat smaller *Camptosaurus* ventured out onto the savannas. The plated stegosaurs dwelt in the forests, feeding on the leaves of trees and bushes. Predatory theropods preyed upon the large herbivorous dinosaurs, while their smaller relatives moved through the dense vegetation in search of more modest quarry. Tortoises and crocodiles of all sizes crept about the earth in large numbers while in the air glided the strange pterosaurs, winged reptiles, at least two types of which are known to have frequented the atoll of Solnhofen. At the same time and in the same place, there lived the famous *Archaeopteryx*, the ancestor of our modern birds, possessing both feathers and teeth. In the undergrowth of the Jurassic jungles, the first mammals slithered unobtrusively by. No larger than shrews or mice, they were mere primitive outlines of the class that would later dominate the world. And far at sea ranged fishes and large reptiles adapted to marine life, like the ichthyosaurs and plesiosaurs.

During Cretaceous times the climates of the northern hemisphere began slowly to diversify. In low-lying areas, temperatures continued on the whole to be warm and the weather mild as during the Jurassic. In western and central Europe, as in Kazakhstan, the flora was still luxuriant and a few flowers must already have enlivened the landscape. Willows, poplars, birches, oaks, maples, walnuts and many other deciduous trees were to be found in increasing numbers among the monotonous forests of the more primitive evergreens. Dinosaurs still lorded it over the animal world, giant *Iguanodons* in western Europe and horned ceratopsians in Mongolia.

But at the beginning of the Cenozoic era, the uplifts which at the end of the Cretaceous period marked the birth of modern mountain systems continued, accentuating the differences of altitude and consequently of climates.

THREE GERMAN CLIMATES

HOT

These drawings show how one place—Germany—responded to climatic change. In the humid Jurassic period 170 million years ago, the warm lagoons were home to Mystriosaurus, an early crocodile.

TEMPERATE

By the Eocene, 50 million years ago, the climate had grown cooler and drier, and tapirlike animals had appeared. The one shown here is Lophiodon, which was about the size of a modern rhinoceros.

COLD

Some time in the last million years, during the extreme cold of the Pleistocene glaciation, woolly mammoths were common in Germany, roaming the tundra which then comprised western Europe.

A general cooling down in temperature was to continue all over the northern hemisphere. In Eocene times, the Arctic Zone had a climate little different from the present Temperate Zone, which now had turned subtropical. Around Paris, for instance, palm trees flourished as well as pines, thujas and evergreens such as laurels, fig trees, magnolias and tree euphorbias. In the swampy forest of the Geisel valley, near Leipzig, sequoias, cypresses and magnolias mixed with palms, breadfruits, cinnamons and mangoes. Small reptiles were abundant in such a damp environment: many lizards—some of them already legless—snakes and turtles and crocodiles. Mammals also were numerous and already quite diversified: an opossum and several lemurs and tarsiers were living among the trees and lianas. Bats were hunting insects over the marshes, and primitive rodents were increasing in number. Among ungulates, primitive lophiodonts resembling tapirs were abundant, together with those distant cousins of the horses, the palaeotheres. In central Asia the climate was more temperate, and elms, beeches, alders, birches, hazels, poplars and walnuts dominated the landscape. Southern Turkestan and Japan, on the contrary, had hot-climate plants.

DURING the Oligocene, winters grew increasingly cold and deciduous trees took over in most parts of Eurasia. The fauna also developed a much more modern appearance, but some strange-looking mammals were still to be found. Such was the case of the giant hornless rhinoceroses, *Paraceratherium* and *Indricotherium*, which were numerous in what is now Mongolia and Kazakhstan. The former is probably the largest of all the land mammals that have ever existed on earth; it stood 16 to 18 feet in height at the shoulders.

By Miocene times the seasonal variations of temperature and the zonation of climates had grown still more marked. In the heart of Eurasia, herbaceous plants for the first time became preponderant, particularly grasses which began to form vast prairies and steppes—an ideal niche to be filled by herbivorous mammals and seed-eating birds and rodents. Primitive antelopes such as *Protragocerus* appeared; primitive deer like *Dicrocerus* and the first giraffid, *Palaeotragus*, very similar to the modern okapi, roamed the plains. Despite the general

ICE AGE VEGETATION

At the height of the Pleistocene glaciation, Eurasia's vegetation was arranged in the pattern shown in the map below. The worst impact of the cold came from the northwest. Scandinavia, the British Isles and parts of Russia and Siberia sank under the icecap, and the highlands were glaciated. A belt of tundra, both marshy and wooded, swept across the continent; conifers flourished in irregular splotches of taiga from the Iberian peninsula to the Pacific. Deciduous forest cloaked the Mediterranean shore, and grasslands and Mediterranean scrub covered broad areas of today's deserts.

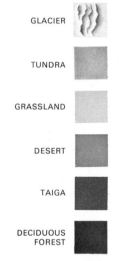

GLACIER

TUNDRA

GRASSLAND

DESERT

TAIGA

DECIDUOUS FOREST

MEDITERRANEAN VEGETATION

cooling temperature, the ancestors of the elephants, previously known only in Africa, made their way to Eurasia.

In the forests of western and southern Europe, higher primates undertook at that time a spectacular evolution. In France, the primitive gibbon, *Pliopithecus*, made its appearance during the middle Miocene, while in Italy we find another famous brachiating ape, the *Oreopithecus*. At about the same time, an advanced manlike ape, the *Dryopithecus*, appeared in Europe and Turkey. But the general temperature continued to drop little by little and the cold in the mountains became severe. During the Pliocene the vegetation of the low-lying areas still retained something of its southern aspect, but as time passed it became sparser, announcing the great over-all cold spell which was soon to transform the whole of Eurasia north of the Pyrenees, the Alps and the Himalayas into a huge Arctic region.

As the temperature fell progressively throughout these 60 or more million years of the Cenozoic era, fundamental changes were wrought in the animal and plant world of the Northern Hemisphere. Ichthyosaurs and other giant aquatic reptiles no longer foraged in the cooling oceans; mammals teemed on the land and dinosaurs were gone forever. Then, during the brief Pleistocene epoch, the cold reached a climax that challenged every Eurasian form of life as it had never been challenged before.

Eurasia had only just achieved its geographic unity and acquired the outlines which we know today when it had to undergo this most dramatic episode of its already eventful history, the Pleistocene glaciations. At four different times waves of intense and lasting cold gripped the greater part of the Northern Hemisphere, emptying the continent of most of its warmth-loving flora and fauna, which either became extinct or migrated toward equatorial latitudes. Gigantic glaciers similar to those to be found today in Greenland and the Antarctic appeared over Scandinavia and on the high mountain chains. These huge ice sheets froze vast quantities of water, and thus lowered the level of the seas, uncovering what is now the highest parts of the continental plateau.

IN these four major frigid periods of glaciation, the ice sheets were not always of the same size. At their maximum extent an immense icecap enveloped Scandinavia, the greater part of the British Isles, Iceland, the Baltic and portions of northern Russia. The great rivers of ice from the central cap streamed radially in all directions; on the west into the Atlantic Ocean, on the north into the Arctic Ocean, on the east over the Kola Peninsula to the Pechora river, on the southeast to Kazan and down the Dnieper and the Don. At the same time the Alpine glaciers grew and grew, creeping down the mountains and out across the plains as far as Lyons, Zurich, Salzburg and Udine. The same thing happened in the Pyrenees, Caucasus, the Himalayas, the Pamirs, the Hindu Kush, the Kunlun, the Altai and highlands east of Lake Baikal and the Lena river. An ice sheet extended from the Lena to the Bering Sea. The melting waters from the Scandinavian ice sheet drained off toward the south and flowed through the Volga into a vast Aralo-Caspian sea. During these ice ages, communication between Europe and Asia was cut off at least once. While the ice was encroaching over the north of the continent, its effects were felt in the south. The climate grew colder in the lower latitudes, and the vegetation zones migrated slowly toward the equator. Trees and other vegetation died off in huge areas which were gradually converted to stretches of tundra surrounding the ice sheets. Forests persisted only in the Mediterranean region, China and Japan. Here and there, places of refuge remained in sheltered regions or in isolated nunataks where certain plants and certain invertebrates managed to find safety even during the peaks of glaciation.

Between icy paroxysms three periods of respite lasting from 60,000 to 190,000 years allowed the southern plants and animals to make temporary incursions toward the north before being forced back again toward the south by renewed offensives of cold. In a few thousand years plants can migrate tremendous distances simply by reseeding themselves and spreading northward or southward as the climate dictates; it was during these interglacials that broad-leaved trees such as the oak, birch, linden, elm, plane, holly and box recolonized the plains of Germany and Belgium, while laurel once more took root along the northern shores of the Mediterranean. As it grew warmer the tundra shrank away to the northward under this green assault, and so did the tundra animals. The woolly rhinoceros, the mammoth, the musk ox, the arctic fox and the white hare, which had roamed widely throughout Europe during the cold spells, were driven inexorably toward the Arctic regions. In the center of the continent the animals of the vast steppes of central Asia—the saiga antelope, the Przewalski's horse, the wild ass, the bobac and the pika—undertook similar advances and retreats and sometimes ventured as far as the Atlantic shores. But because of the physical structure of Eurasia, each onslaught of cold had a devastating effect on the distribution of living forms. Southern species which had existed in comfort north of the mountain barrier during warm cycles of the climate had a serious problem when the weather turned cold. They could not simply drift southward indefinitely as animals did in North America during the ice ages; they were trapped on the wrong side of the Alps or the Himalayas, with no way to get through. Others could not cross the Mediterranean into Africa. The few that did get through had an equally hard time repopulating the northern areas after the weather turned warm again. For this reason, each glacial episode took its toll of southern species, and the result was a drastic reduction both in numbers and in types throughout Palearctic Eurasia.

Since the end of the last ice age some 10,000 years ago, the climate of Palearctic Eurasia has shown a gradual warming up tendency interrupted only by a few cold episodes in which certain mountain glaciers extended and temporarily closed some of the Alpine and Himalayan passes. Within historical memory there have been four of these slight climatic fluctuations: a warm period, culminating between about 5000 and 3000 B.C.; a cooler climatic epoch culminating between 900 and 450 B.C.; a second warm spell in the Middle Ages around 1000 to 1200 A.D., and the "little ice age" between about 1430 and 1850 A.D. None seriously affected the flora and fauna, which by now had largely stabilized —except for the effects wrought by man—into the pattern we know today.

THE story of Eurasia, the land that slowly and with many retrogressions rose out of two primeval seas, shows that this supercontinent is to a great extent a newcomer in the history of our planet. Geologically, its unity is a recent phenomenon. In the course of succeeding geological eras some of its component parts have often had closer contacts with other continents—Africa and North America in particular—than they had with each other. These parts were widely different worlds which finally became welded by the great Tertiary uplifts into a single mass. Instead of being the cradle of life and thought which our fathers liked to fancy, Eurasia was and is a meeting point of multiple and, at times, even conflicting influences, as we shall presently see.

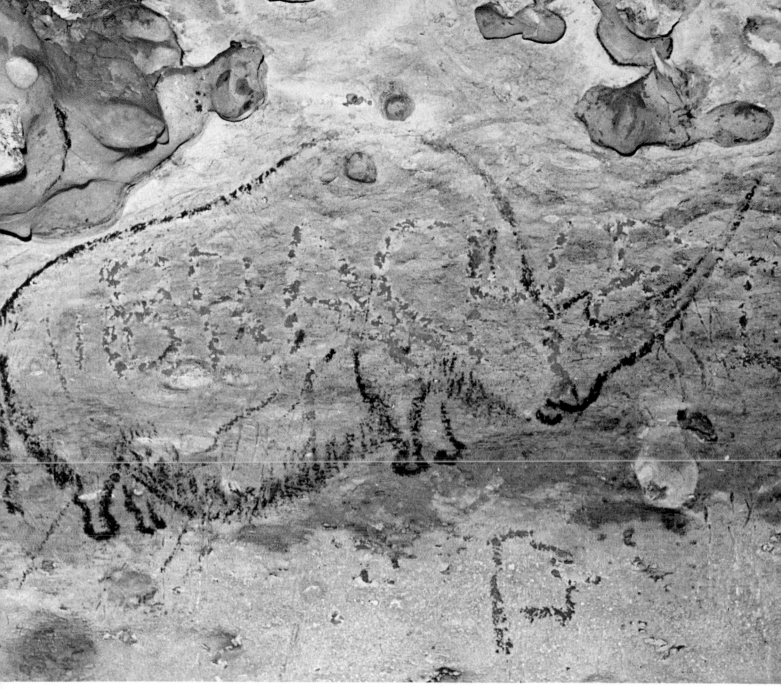

THIS WOOLLY RHINOCEROS ON A CAVE WALL WAS A FAMILIAR BEAST TO THE ICE AGE MAN OF FRANCE WHO DREW IT SOME 15,000 YEARS AGO

A Gallery of Ancestors

When the last ice age ended in Eurasia some 10,000 years ago, the age of man's civilization began. Hunting with weapons, cooking with fire, clearing forests and tilling fields, men laid siege to the land and made the first great changes in the natural order. But they also produced artists who left for their descendants a record of the animals among which they lived—some no longer in existence.

17

ATLANTIC OCEAN

NORTH SEA

BALTIC SEA

BLACK SEA

CASPIAN SEA

ARAL SEA

TURKESTAN DESERT

IRANIAN DESERT

MEDITERRANEAN SEA

SAHARA DESERT

RED SEA

PERSIAN GULF

ARABIAN DESERT

ARABIAN

THE LIFE ZONES OF
PALEARCTIC
EURASIA

TUNDRA

CONIFEROUS FOREST

DECIDUOUS FOREST

PRAIRIE STEPPE

DRY STEPPE

DESERT

MEDITERRANEAN SCRUB

THE WORLD'S BIGGEST LAND MASS, the continent of Eurasia spreads halfway around the globe. This map highlights the portion known as Palearctic Eurasia, which has its own characteristic flora and fauna and extends from Iceland to Japan, and from the Sahara to Siberia. The Palearctic's southern reaches are delimited by the pink line. In Southeast Asia the line is broken to indicate that this is a transitional area, without barriers to impede dispersion of species. The line skirts

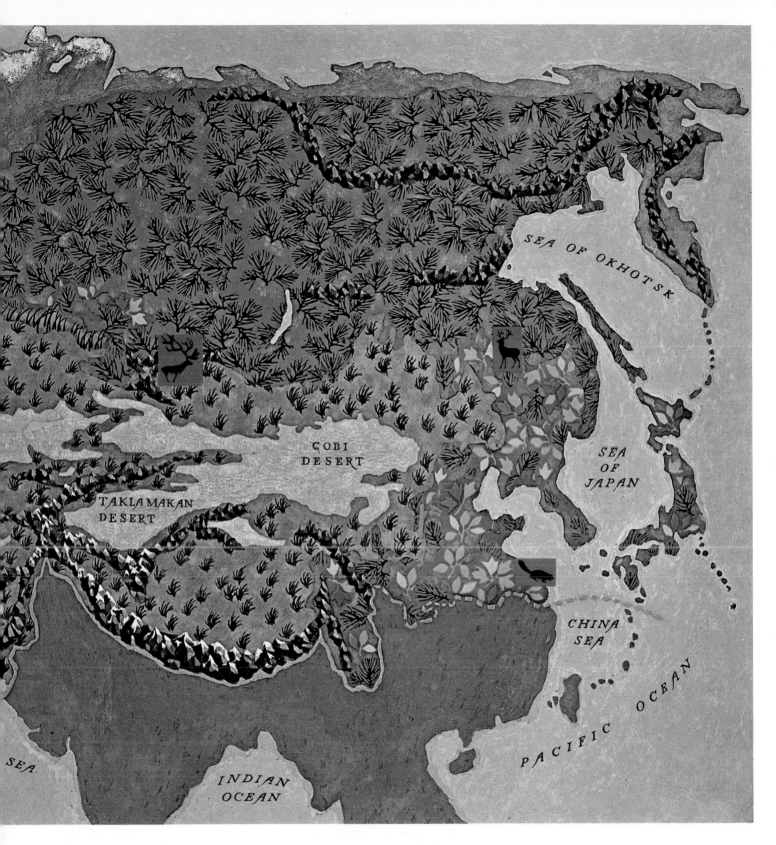

SEA OF OKHOTSK

SEA OF JAPAN

GOBI DESERT

TAKLAMAKAN DESERT

CHINA SEA

PACIFIC OCEAN

SEA

INDIAN OCEAN

the Himalayas, crosses the Arabian peninsula and terminates in the Red Sea rather than in Africa, since ecologists disagree about whether to include the Sahara in the Palearctic.

The map shows a pristine Eurasia—the land as it would be if it had not suffered man's depredations. Its bands of vegetation, keyed at left, represent plants that would dominate in any one climatic zone if given the chance. In at least one area, man's influence has been to the good: the desert around the

Caspian Sea is arable today, the result of extensive irrigation.

Along with the vegetation symbols, silhouettes of various animals taken from works of art, many of which date back thousands of years, also give a hint of what life was like in the past. The silhouettes are placed on the map according to where the objects themselves were discovered. On the pages that follow, photographs in color show the full beauty of these treasures—and reveal the wild Eurasia that our ancestors knew.

19

RED-BREASTED GEESE, shown in the oldest extant Egyptian painting, adorned the tomb of Itet on the Nile. These birds, which breed in Siberia, occasionally still winter in Egypt.

WITH FLAILING WINGS, a flock of waterfowl flees before the attack of a hunter stalking the papyrus-lined banks of an Egyptian stream. This scene was inlaid in gold and alloy on a dagger some 3,500 years ago.

A Field Guide to the Past

Closeness to nature was a necessity to early man, and even as he progressed along the road to civilization, he kept his ties with the plants and animals upon which his existence so heavily depended. Intimate knowledge and admiration for many of them is evident in much of his art: so meticulous were the best of the early painters and sculptors that many of the animals they portrayed can easily be related to those of the modern world.

Thus the red-breasted geese at left, painted in Egypt 4,600 years ago, find their counterparts in Roger Tory Peterson's *A Field Guide to the Birds of Britain and Europe*. The bull's head at right, carved in ancient Crete, shows some characteristics similar to the black fighting bulls of Spain today. And on a Mycenaean dagger an ancient craftsman has caught forever an incident still common to the modern world: by a stream, a slender carnivore—perhaps of the cat family, perhaps a mongoose relative—is chasing waterfowl while a school of fish swims by.

CRETAN BULL'S HEAD, executed in soapstone, with crystal eyes and horns of gilded wood, was used to pour libations on the altar at Knossos. Though a domestic breed, the bull shows many aurochs features.

LION OF BABYLON stalks the Processional Way built by Nebuchadnezzar in the Sixth Century B.C. This may be an Asiatic lion, prevalent at that time all the way from India to Turkey.

LION OF LEGEND is strangled by Hercules in this classic Greek vase painting of 525 B.C. Lions were plentiful in ancient Greece, but by around 80 to 100 A.D. they had been hunted to extinction there.

LIONS OF PERSIA form the hilt of a dagger dating from about 400 B.C. Lions hung on in the Middle East up to the 19th Century, when their numbers shrank drastically. The last known kill was in 1923.

LIONESS OF CRETE appears in the form of a ritual vessel, carved around 1450 B.C. in limestone, from the palace in Knossos. Lions were often associated with the mother goddess.

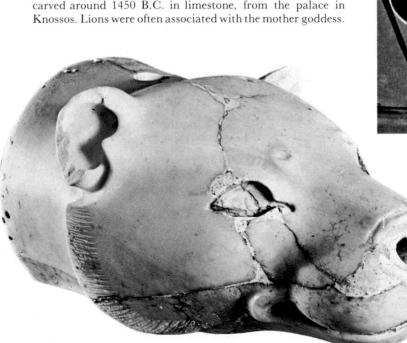

Lions of Antiquity

There is more than symbolic significance in the powerful portrayal above of Hercules vanquishing the Nemean lion: man has indeed driven this majestic animal from all but a small part of its original range. Within historic times, Asiatic lions roamed all of the Middle East and seem to have even reached southeastern Europe; they are mentioned 130 times in the Scriptures alone. Symbol of the sun and much admired for its strength and courage, the Asiatic lion was considered fit game for royalty. Guns hastened its demise, and today the species is found wild only in a small game preserve in western India.

HOODED CROWS of an old Arabic fable harass their traditional enemies, the owls. Adaptable and easily recognizable birds, they are still found throughout the Middle East and Russia and along the borders of Europe.

Symbols and Legends

When King Peroz I of Persia went hunting 15 centuries ago, he was performing a ritual act deeply rooted in the ancient history of his country. His quarry, as shown on the gilded silver plate at right, was the wild sheep that once roamed the forests of Persia, but now survives there only in remote mountain fastnesses. The Persians believed that such sheep, along with goats and bulls, were living representatives of the moon, since their crescent horns described its shape during one of its phases. They also believed that a god-power in the sky governed the movements of heavenly bodies and that the moon, under the direction of this power, gave moisture to their arid land. Thus the king, as the representative of the power on earth, could scarcely perform a deed with more symbolic significance than hunting down the moon animals—thereby affirming his dominion over them.

RITUAL HUNTS, a feature of court life, occupied Persian royalty of the Sasanian era (224-650 A.D.). Driven across the path of the royal party by beaters, game stood little chance of escaping destruction.

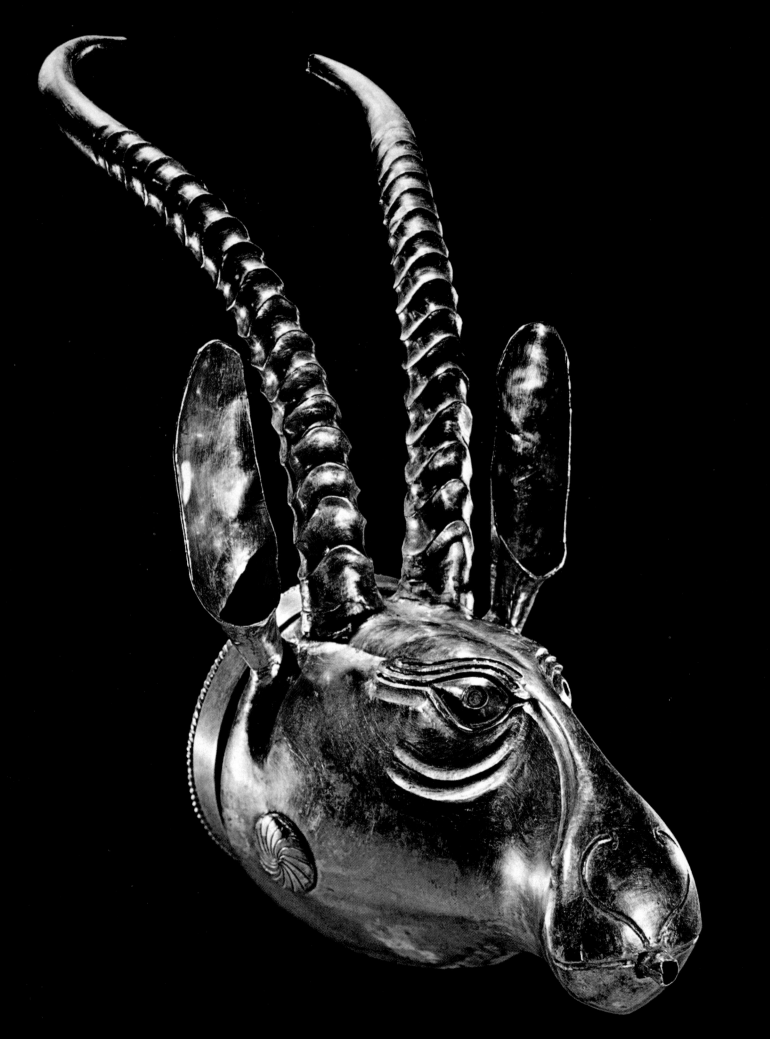

The Toll of the Hunter

No records exist to indicate how many wild animals have been crowded out or hunted to destruction in that part of the Middle East which man calls the cradle of his civilization. It is certain that Paleolithic man hunted deer, gazelle and goat 25,000 years ago in what is today Iran. Later, with the spread of agriculture, the introduction of the riding horse and chariot, and the growth of city-states, the pressure on larger grazing animals grew to the point where many faced extermination. The royal hunts, in particular, carried on for over 2,000 years, were affairs of enormous slaughter. An Assyrian king of the Ninth Century B. C. boasted thus of his prowess: "... by my stretched-out arm and through my furious courage, 15 mighty lions from the mountains and the woods in my hand I captured, and 50 lion cubs I carried away. . . . Alive in my hands I captured . . . herds of wild oxen and elephants and lions . . . and birds . . . beasts and wild asses, and gazelles, and stags. . . . Thirty elephants . . . I slew and 250 mighty wild oxen . . . I laid low, and 370 mighty lions." No man to waste game, the king gave a feast at which 500 deer and 500 gazelles were served, in addition to 1,000 cattle and 15,000 sheep.

A PERSIAN WILD GOAT painted on a 5,600-year-old vase has characteristic beard and knobby horns. Ranging from the Caucasus through mountains of Asia Minor, it is still hunted.

THE SAIGA ANTELOPE (*left*) of the steppe is portrayed here in a Persian drinking vessel of the Sixth Century. Its horns nearly caused its extinction because of their "medicinal" value.

ASSYRIAN DEER are driven into a net in a Seventh Century B. C. bas-relief from the palace at Nineveh. Three species survive in modern Iraq: the red, the roe and the fallow deer.

A STYLIZED REINDEER was carved in wood and gilded by a Scythian around the Fifth Century B.C. Male deer were revered by Scythians, who believed that they carried souls of the dead to the beyond.

28

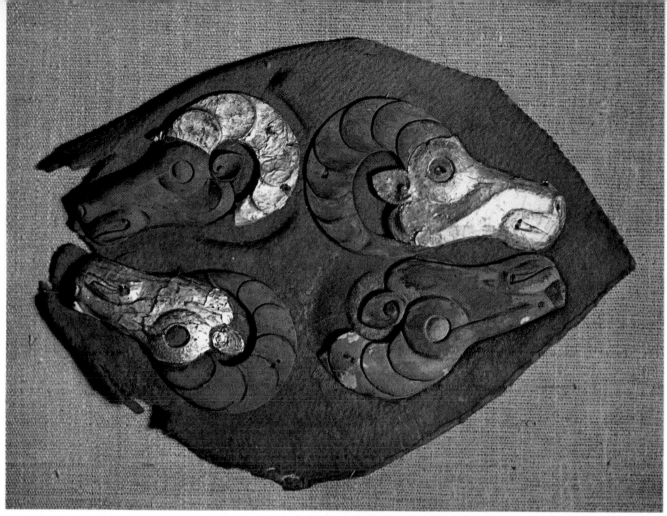

FOUR RAMS' HEADS ON A BIT OF SADDLE LEATHER FROM A SCYTHIAN TOMB COULD WELL HAVE BEEN INSPIRED BY EAST ASIATIC WILD SHEEP

Some Animals the Nomads Knew

The close ties of a nomad people with the animals on which their lives depend speaks everywhere from the art of the ancient Scythians. Central Asian tribes who expanded southwestward between 800 and 700 B.C., finally to occupy the Black Sea region, the Scythians were skilled horsemen and fierce warriors given to taking scalps, drinking their victims' blood and making cups out of their skulls. On seasonal migrations they encountered creatures of the vast grasslands and mountain barriers, and it was these animals that they used as subjects for their vigorous art. The rich trappings with which the Scythians draped and decorated their clothing, horses and funeral wagons included stylized stags, leopards, lions, wolves, mountain goats, swans, eagles and others. Many such relics—some as perishable as the ones shown here—survive today. This is due largely to the fact that numerous Scythian tombs, dug into mountain slopes and covered over with logs, stones and earth, soon became permanently frostbound, thus serving as deep freezes.

A FALLOW DEER has its antlers sheathed in leather. These deer, originally a southern species, were probably encountered by the Scythians in the Black Sea and Caspian regions.

統山采熟蹲
枝嘗五技可
妙用所長自
是託身遠害
室不須老吏
晏張湯
己卯春月
術題

SEVEN CENTURIES AGO CH'IEN HSÜAN, A SCHOLAR AND CIVIL SERVANT, PAINTED A SQUIRREL IN THE HILLS NEAR THE MOUTH OF THE YANGTZE

An Alien but Familiar World

One of the fascinating aspects of Eurasia is that, although two of mankind's most widely differentiated cultures—Occident and Orient—lie at its opposite ends, these two extremes are firmly united in a single land mass. With climate a common factor in the distribution of plants and animals, the temperate areas of the Far East are little different from those of Europe. Hence the scenes shown here from the scrolls of ancient Chinese painters appear exotic only in terms of style: deer in an autumn-tinged forest of maple trees, a squirrel on the fruit-laden branch of a peach tree. The difference today is that much of the woodland habitat of the Asiatic red deer has been destroyed and converted to agricultural uses, so that the deer has retreated to the wilder mountainsides and valleys. The more adaptable squirrel, however, remains familiar to the Far East, as does its counterpart to Europe 5,000 miles away.

THE PERT DEER SHOWN IN THIS 1,000-YEAR-OLD PAINTING ARE FOUND TODAY MAINLY IN THE MOUNTAINS OF CENTRAL ASIA

SNOW-CAPPED HEIGHTS of the Himalayas (*opposite*) determine rainfall in the plains of Kashmir, where poplars and lush meadows abound. The map above, like those that will be found at the heads of other chapters, is colored to indicate the area described in the chapter.

2

The Southern Barriers

IN the turbulent history of Eurasia, two major phenomena, more than any others, profoundly influenced the distribution of vegetation and animal life. The first was the continued existence, through most of geologic time, of the Tethys, that east-west sea which once stretched from Gibraltar to the Timor Sea and has left us among its remnants today the Mediterranean and the Persian Gulf. The other, occurring some 36 million years ago in Tertiary times, was the birth of a great mountain belt also lying roughly in an east-west direction between the Indian and Siberian shields: the Himalayan chain.

When we think of the Himalayas today, we tend to think principally of isolated parts of this range—the areas of Everest, Annapurna, Nanga Parbat and the other superlative peaks which have for so long been a challenge to ambitious mountaineers. Actually, the full scope of the Himalayan chain encompasses a great deal more. It is an immense succession of peaks stretching from the borders of the Soviet Union and Afghanistan in the west all the way to the Indian-Chinese border north of Burma in the east—a distance of about 1,500 miles. Just as the waters of the Tethys Sea constituted a wide barrier preventing the plants and animals of Africa and India from moving northward into the

Eurasian area, so did the Himalayas with their snowy summits form an equally uncrossable boundary cutting off the boreal flora and fauna from the rich tropical world of south and southeast Asia.

Looking at this incalculable pile of heaved-up rock, it is hard to believe that it once lay at the bottom of the sea. But the presence of marine fossils throughout the range indicates that this is so. How long the Himalayas will endure is impossible to say. The Tethys and Uralian seas have come and gone, as we have seen, and other mountain ranges which, for all we know, may once have been as lofty as the Himalayas have been ground flat over the millennia. But the sheer bulk of this enormous heap of mountains, standing like a backbone athwart the world's largest continent, is so impressive that it is tempting to assert that it will endure as long as the earth itself.

The effect of the twin barriers of water and mountain chain can be seen through all the natural history of Eurasia. There have been east-west migrations between Eurasia and North America, as witness the horses and the camels. There may have been some minor south-to-north migration of plants and animals in the area of the Mediterranean itself, but all along the southern limits of the continent, from the Atlantic eastward, the only major free-passage zone was the plains of eastern China.

The present Eurasian continent is therefore subdivided into two biogeographical regions which are as distinct as they can be from one another. The northern zone, known as the Palearctic region, includes northwest Africa and most of the Arabian peninsula but is mainly comprised of Europe and the whole of Asia north of the Himalayas; it is this vast area which forms the subject matter of this book. The southern zone, called the Oriental region, includes the Indian subcontinent, the Indo-Chinese peninsula and the Malay Archipelago. Despite the geographical unity of these two areas, the ecological border between them, stretching from the Atlantic to China's Yunnan province, is still a total barrier of mountain, desert and sea, crossed only each spring and fall by a few hundred species of migratory birds. That these are undaunted by even the highest mountains is shown by the fact that some of them have been observed flying straight over the topmost Himalayan chains—the mountaineer George Lowe once saw a formation of bar-headed geese passing over the summit of Everest itself!

THE MOUNTAIN BARRIERS

The great ice sheets which pushed down from the north in the Pleistocene glaciations drove many animals south to warmer parts of Europe, Africa and Asia. There, after the ice retreated, they were trapped by mountain and sea barriers—an east-west wall running right across Eurasia—that prevented their return. Only along the coast of China was there a broad passage (shown in color) where animals could repopulate the north. The smaller colored areas in Europe and the Middle East show where some animals in the Mediterranean region managed to trickle back through passes in the Pyrenees, Alps and Near East ranges.

TODAY the Himalayas, particularly in the mountains of Tibet and southwestern China, harbor some of the most interesting wildlife in the world—and also some of the least known. The physical difficulties of penetrating this region and the fact that as a frontier area it has only rarely been opened to European or American naturalists explain why so few scientific expeditions have traveled there. A considerable amount of collecting was carried out between 1860 and 1939 by explorers and traveling naturalists, but these, like the universally famous Major General Nicolai Mikhailovich Przewalski, were usually unable to stay on for any prolonged period in such inhospitable country. Only such missionary naturalists as the Fathers Armand David, Jean Marie Delavay and Jean André Soulié, and such bold "plant hunters" in quest of spectacular species as E. H. Wilson, George Forrest, Reginald Farrer, Frank Kingdon Ward and Joseph F. Rock, stayed there for any length of time or repeated their journeys.

The vegetation of this huge mountainous zone is one of the most remarkable and most attractive to be found anywhere. Furthermore, because of the abrupt changes in altitude, it is also one of the most varied. In the mountains of Szechwan at the eastern end of the Himalayas, tropical flora such as palms and bamboos as well as rice crops can be found up to about 2,000 feet. Above that and up to 5,000 feet, the slopes, when not cultivated by man, are covered with a temperate rain forest largely made up of evergreen oaks, laurels, hollies, China firs and pines. There is also a rich undergrowth of ferns. Between 5,000 and 10,000 feet there is a cool temperate zone characterized by a mixed forest in which deciduous trees and shrubs mingle with conifers—a landscape not unlike America's Appalachians or Ozarks. Between 10,000 and 11,500 feet is a subalpine zone of magnificent stands of coniferous trees mixed with great rhododendron bushes. The timber line is at about 12,000 feet. Above it an alpine zone reaches as high as 16,000 feet, characterized by moorlands and grasslands carpeted with many flowering plants, among them primulas, gentians, poppies, small-leaved rhododendrons and barberries. Highest of all, at 17,500 feet begin the permanent snows.

THIS striking and often awesomely beautiful landscape changes as one travels westward. On the high, bare Tibetan plateau, the flora is considerably poorer, but it still includes a variety of members of the pea family—herbs like the milk vetch and locoweed—and curious composites such as *Saussurea* as well as edelweiss and groundsel. And as the great range curves southward, it enters the regions of increased rainfall. The tropical vegetation climbs higher on the first slopes and once again flourishes on the valley sides, though it is still not comparable to that of the mountains of southwestern China. In the western Himalayas the first cedars, the deodars, begin to appear, advance patrols of those to be found in Lebanon and North Africa. Above the coniferous forests, quantities of rhododendrons of all colors flaunt their floral glory. In the alpine meadows strange wild rhubarb, brilliant primroses and blue or yellow poppies strike notes of vibrant color.

The wildlife of the enormous central-Asiatic mountain block is by far the most spectacular of the whole of Palearctic Eurasia. It comprises a number of animal species about whose ways of life next to nothing is known. These creatures, many of them among the world's rarest, owe their survival up till now to the inaccessibility of the regions they inhabit and the sparse human population there. But these conditions are changing rapidly and it is increasingly apparent that unless definite steps are taken to ensure the proper preservation of endangered habitats, many of the most interesting Himalayan species will follow Africa's game animals along the road to extinction. Despite the scarcity of recent or reliable scientific observation, it is still clear that each of the large animals which give to this part of the world its unique character keeps to a specific environment, outside of which it cannot survive. While this is generally true of most animals everywhere, what lends it particular importance in this part of Eurasia is something unique to mountain communities: an extreme interlocking of habitats and a rapid succession of vegetation belts stacked one above the other along the valley sides.

The Himalayas, rising from a tropical floor to the highest peaks in the world, offer environments which correspond to all climatic zones. Moreover, because they rise so steeply, the mountainsides are divided and subdivided into belts of vegetation which are comparatively narrow in extent yet extremely rich in the communities they contain. This gives them a beauty and fascination rarely found elsewhere—but it also makes them more vulnerable than other areas

PLANTS OF THE HEIGHTS

RHUBARB

Among the plants thriving in the rarefied atmosphere of the Himalayas are rhubarbs, represented here by Rheum nobile. They live on moraines and in sheltered valleys, from 13,000 to over 14,000 feet above sea level. A more exotic plant, Saussurea leucocoma (below), grows even higher up, to an altitude of 19,000 feet. Dotting the windswept Tibetan plateau, it hugs the ground closely and wears a cottony coat for insulation against the loss of heat and moisture. A tiny hole on the top of the plant allows pollinating bumblebees to crawl down inside.

SAUSSUREA

which provide greater scope to their plant and animal communities. The high plateau with its great altitudes may still be relatively safe from human depredation, but lower down it is a different story. Already roads are on the increase, villages are growing in number and population, and the heavy hand of commercial enterprise is encroaching on the land. The forests of Szechwan, for example, constitute the greater part of the timber wealth of a China whose population is increasing rapidly along with its industrial capacity—a potentially fatal combination of circumstances, as was proven in America's Northwest half a century ago.

The extreme zonation of the biotic communities in Szechwan and eastern Tibet is clearly demonstrated by the observations of the German ornithologist Ernst Schäfer, the last Western naturalist to make a detailed study of this formerly remote corner of Eurasia. In the Hsifan range east of Tatsienlu, a traditional frontier town known today as Kangting, the vegetation belts and their associated animals follow each other in quick succession on the mountain slopes. There, communities with the widest imaginable differences are ranged one upon another. At the bottoms of the arid, stony valleys, from 3,000 to 6,000 feet above sea level, the typical mammal is the goral, a stocky, goatlike animal with coarse hair forming a small crest on its neck and with short backward-curling horns. It lives in small groups of two to 12 individuals. When frightened, it utters a hissing sound.

The goral prefers open ground and thus is seldom seen above 6,000 feet, because at that point the rocky slopes turn into a dense bamboo forest which flourishes in a thick band up to 8,000 feet. There lives the famous giant panda, discovered by Father David in 1869. One might say that this "unique carnivore," as it was at first called, is a mixture of bear and raccoon. It resembles the former in its stocky limbs, plantigrade feet and short tail. Its color scheme is startling—mostly white, with brownish black limbs and ears and a small black patch around each eye. But despite its broad and massive skull equipped with heavy crushing teeth, this misnamed "carnivore" of frightening appearance eats no meat; its strictly vegetarian habits are attested to by its droppings, which are shaped like eggs five to seven inches long and composed of partly digested bamboo shoots. The panda's paw, moreover, presents a curious adaptation which allows it better to handle the smooth stems of its favorite vegetable food. An additional bone, a sesamoid, is so enlarged that it acts as an extra sixth finger which can be opposed to the other five.

The giant panda is extremely rare and very few have been brought to the Western world. Mrs. Ruth Harkness, wife of the American explorer William H. Harkness Jr., brought the first—and most famous—giant panda out of China in 1936, wrapping the young animal in her fur coat to simulate its mother. This panda was given to Chicago's Brookfield Zoo. The Bronx Zoo's first giant panda, named Pandora, delighted thousands of visitors at the 1939 New York World's Fair. Madame Chiang Kai-shek presented two more to the Bronx Zoo in 1941.

IN the same bamboo jungle and the tree zone immediately above it lives the giant panda's near relation, the lesser panda, whose appearance and diet, however, are completely different. This animal looks like a large cat with a roundish head, big pointed ears and a long tail. Its coat is generally a lovely rust of deep chestnut hue and it has a white snout and black paws and underbelly. The lesser panda is resolutely omnivorous: it searches for

**THE WET AND THE DRY
IN THE HIMALAYAS**

The summer winds that sweep in from the Indian Ocean are heavy with moisture picked up from the sea. They drench the lowlands, and as they ride up the Himalayan slopes, they cool and lose most of their remaining moisture in the form of heavy falls of snow. Wrung dry, there is little moisture left for the far slopes; they remain unwatered in winter too, since the prevailing wind then is a cold dry norther.

roots, succulent grasses, leaves and fallen fruits as well as for insects. The young are born in the spring, usually in the hollow of a tree or the crevice of a rock. The adults spend their days sleeping in trees, curled up in a ball in the topmost branches, their bushy tails wrapped round their heads. Pairs and family parties forage for food only during the night.

Within this same belt in the Hsifan range lives still another animal, another discovery of Father David's, which is among the rarest known: the orange snub-nosed monkey (*Rhinopithecus roxellanae*). Related to the langurs, this monkey can be distinguished at first sight by its peculiar turned-up, prominent nose and its beautiful coloring. In the male, the face and nose are blue, the eyes brown, the neck, back, top of head and tail grayish black, while the underparts, forehead, ears, sides of the head and neck, limbs, hands and feet are reddish golden. The females' coloring is more toned down, and the young, when newly born, are a light buff.

FINALLY, ranging from the dense bamboo jungle to the firs and rhododendrons which continue above it to a height of 10,000 feet, is a strange ungulate, the takin, whose appearance is the most peculiar of all the goat-antelopes (*Rupicaprini*). This clumsy animal, which looks neither like a goat nor an antelope, has horns which rise from near the midline of its head and then curve abruptly outward to finish in a backward and upward sweep. From the unusual shape of its horns, the takin looks as if it might be some relative of the wildebeest or the musk ox, though this is not at all the case. Its muzzle is convex and covered with hair, its neck tremendously thick, while its body is supported by extremely stout legs. Its shaggy fur varies from a dull straw color to a blackish brown, the calves being almost black. These strange creatures live in small groups in the winter, but in the summer congregate in large herds of several hundred head. During this season they reach higher altitudes, sometimes climbing to as high as 14,000 feet. Rutting takes place in July and calves are dropped toward the end of March or early April.

Between the timber line and the snow fields, from 15,000 to 18,000 feet, lives another ungulate which never enters scrub or forest—the bharal, or blue sheep. The general color of its head and upper parts is brownish gray, suffused with slatey blue—colors that blend perfectly in any season with the blue shale and rocks of the open hillsides where the blue sheep lives. This animal is a curious combination of the wild sheep and the wild goat. Like a sheep, it grazes on open grassy slopes, but like a goat it is a good climber and does not hesitate to take to precipitous cliffs. In summer, blue sheep are said to live in mixed flocks ranging from fewer than 10 to as many as 400, with mature males keeping somewhat to themselves. The really old rams spend the summer at higher levels, joining the females and younger males in September or October, when the rutting season begins.

The bird life of these same mountains in western Szechwan is in many cases as strange as the mammals we have just described. Pheasants are represented by many strikingly beautiful species. Around 9,000 feet in the rhododendron jungle of the Hsifan mountains, for instance, lives Temminck's tragopan, which Major J. K. Stanford once christened "the great Beau Brummell of a bird." The male has a stunningly variegated crimson plumage, and when displaying itself during courtship, puffs up two small, fleshy, bright-blue horns which are normally concealed in the feathers on each side of the crown. Heightening this unusual display, it also inflates a neck pouch of bright-blue skin with salmon-pink blotches round its margin. These markings somewhat resemble the Chinese calligraphic character for longevity, and the tragopans are considered birds of good omen. The female is a more discreet mottled brown. These birds feed largely on fern leaves, but eat also acorns and buds.

Considerably higher up, well above the deciduous forest in alpine meadows between 14,000 and 16,000 feet, lives the Chinese monal, a rare representative of the most brilliantly garbed group of pheasants. The metallic glints of blue, purple, green and red hues in these birds are equalled only by the brilliance of the hummingbirds of South America; the Chinese have aptly named them the "fowl of burning charcoal." During the day, Chinese monals are found in small parties, with males and females sometimes forming separate companies, frequenting the open rocky meadows and feeding on roots, tubers and other vegetable substances which they dig with their strong beaks—never with their feet as many other birds do. At night they descend to perch either in the scrubby, stunted rhododendrons or in the pines still farther down.

Very different from these colorful birds and animals is the fauna of the high Tibetan plateau whose windy, desolate steppes begin at the head of the high valley of the Yangtze, only a hundred miles west of Kangting. Contrary to what one might think, these seemingly limitless stretches do not constitute a homogeneous habitat, since they become increasingly arid as one travels north. Three distinct environmental belts are discernible, named by Ernst Schäfer for the big mammals most frequently found there: the Tibetan Gazelle Steppe, the Kiang Steppe and the Wild Yak Steppe.

The most southerly of the three is the Tibetan Gazelle Steppe. Here, at an average altitude of about 12,000 feet, are the most favorable climate and a four- to five-month growing season for vegetation. The flora is relatively rich; wide stretches of various grasses enable nomad herdsmen to pasture their flocks, and several types of edelweiss and even some buckthorn bushes and dwarf rhododendrons are to be found.

The climate turns ruder in the Kiang Steppe, where the land slopes up to an average altitude of 14,000 feet. Vegetation is sparser, although the landscape is still brightened here and there during the summer season by the golden flower of a lovely species of poppy native to the area.

Finally, still farther north, the immense desert plains of the Wild Yak Steppe stretch away as far as the distant Marco Polo range. Here, at altitudes fluctuating between 14,500 to 20,000 feet, is a virtual wilderness where extremely low temperatures allow only two or three months for the sparse grasses to grow in the moister hollows.

So harsh and remote is the Tibetan plateau that little is known about the habits of the larger mammals that live there. The Tibetan gazelle, for which the first environmental belt is named, is a small, slender species, standing about as high as a collie at the shoulder. Its coat is a uniformly brownish gray devoid of any facial markings or lateral stripes; the belly and inner sides of its legs are white. Its dun coat blends almost perfectly into the landscape; it is seldom seen, even though it usually congregates in flocks.

A much bigger animal is the kiang, or Tibetan wild ass, chief inhabitant of the next environmental belt. The adult approaches 900 pounds in weight and stands over three feet high. The kiang, in many respects, seems to stand somewhere between the wild asses and the wild horses: it is almost as big as a horse and neighs like one, but it has the squat head of an ass, a short, stocky neck, erect mane and a mulelike tail, long and thin with a tassel of hair at the end. Its coat is reddish gray with white at the nose, throat, chest and belly. From its black mane to the tip of the tail runs a very plainly marked black line. Males and females live together during the coldest season, but as soon as the weather becomes less severe, the old stallions detach themselves from the rest to form small bands ranging from two to 10 animals, which forage together until the rutting season. The females and their foals, together with the younger males, meanwhile wander in herds of 20 to 40 individuals. Rutting takes place at the end of August or early September and the females foal toward the end of July or beginning of August. Like most of the other ungulates of the high plateaus of central Asia, the kiangs shed their thick coats of hair only once a year, during the summer months.

Roaming far to the northward over desolate plateaus that rise as high as 20,000 feet is the most imposing of all Tibetan animals, the wild yak. A big adult male killed by Ernst Schäfer weighed close to 2,000 pounds; the smaller females may attain a weight of 700 pounds. This massively built animal, which is sometimes more than six feet tall at the shoulder among males, has a drooping head, high, humped shoulders and short, sturdy limbs. Its almost uniformly blackish-brown coat of long, coarse hair forms shaggy fringes which hang from its flanks, shoulders and thighs. Beneath that superficial layer lies a dense underfur, soft and closely matted, assuring additional warmth in wintertime, when the temperature drops as low as $-40°F$. In the spring, this underfur comes away in great masses, giving the animals a rough and unkempt appearance. The bull's horns are much more massive than those of any of its domestic relatives. The old males remain aloof for the most part or congregate in small groups of two to five, but the females, the calves and the young males gather in herds numbering anywhere from 20 to 2,000 head. Rutting takes place from September to October and leads to fierce battles between the males.

IN the same desolate environment also dwells the chiru, or Tibetan antelope, a very strange animal indeed. Slight and delicately built, with long, slender horns diverging toward the tips and curving slightly forward, a swollen muzzle and a body covered with dense wool, this odd-looking creature is further characterized by its unusually developed inguinal glands. The color of its coat is variable, most often pale fawn on top and white lower down; its entire face is black and it has a black stripe down the front of each leg. Females are hornless. The chiru, seldom seen, is thought to live in small bands which may consist exclusively of bucks or of bucks and does together. When resting, chirus excavate hollows in which they are also believed to have their young.

The most graceful of the species which inhabit these high steppes is the argali, or great Tibetan sheep, also a dweller of the mountain masses which emerge here and there to break the monotony of the endless plateaus. Although its legs are long and its hoofs small, the argali has a body as bulky as that of a small pony. The summer coat of the ram is reddish brown, darker on the withers, while the rump, throat, chest, belly and inside of the legs are white. Their horns never exceed a single circle, but the old males develop a white ruff about the neck, much of which is shed in the summer coat. Females have little or no mane. The winter coat is paler in both sexes. Argalis wander endlessly in search of the scanty herbage, sometimes as high as 16,000 feet. They may weigh up to 250 pounds, and seem to be a favorite prey of wolves and brown bears, which are the two great carnivores of the Tibetan plains.

On plateau and mountainside, the bird life of Tibet is rich in species of its own. Gallinaceous birds abound: a partridge (*Perdix hodgsoniae*), which is a near relation of the European gray partridge; the snow partridge; the Tibetan snow-cock, which makes its nest in the highest altitudes. The ibisbill, a good-sized shore bird with a long, curved red beak, lives among the stones alongside rocky mountain torrents where its gray plumage and rounded shape provide a per-fect camouflage.

Passerine birds are numerous. A small crow, a ground jay, various larks, rosy finches, snow finches and some accentors mingle with various redstarts and the grandala, found at altitudes up to 17,000 feet. Many water birds are found on the plateau. Scattered at intervals are small swamps and lakes, where such species as the bar-headed goose, the black-necked crane and the brown-headed gull may be found. Occasionally the soft, mournful cry of the solitary snipe may be heard echoing across the steely water.

IN the extreme western areas of the Himalayas and the Pamirs, both flora and fauna are again quite different from those of the Tibetan plateau and the high mountains of western China—and in their way, just as extraordinary. This is the homeland of a majestic subspecies of the argali, the famous Marco Polo sheep. The magnificent horns of the rams are deeply wrinkled and the color of old ivory. They curve in an almost complete circle and finish by ex-tending outward in a bold sweep. The most spectacular of all the wild goats is the markhor. The old males carry tremendous twisted horns which vary widely in different local populations. According to S. H. Prater, the horns of the mar-khors living in the mountains of north Afghanistan assume a true corkscrew pattern whereas those inhabiting Astor farther east diverge widely to form an open spiral. The winter coat is an iron gray which gives way in the summer to a coat of reddish brown. Adult males have a flowing beard and an imposing mane that falls from their necks and shoulders right down to their knees. The older bucks often turn more or less white.

Markhors appear to be remarkably adaptable and live under widely varying conditions. In Astor they range mainly in the open, but in other ranges they inhabit dense pine and birch forests, and yet in still other areas they live on barren slopes. In any case, they seldom go higher than the snow line, probably due to the fact that, unlike the true wild goats, they do not possess an undercoat of wool to protect them against extreme cold.

Working still westward through the peaks and high plateaus, we have now reached the last outposts of the Pamirs—the western end of the great range. The biogeographical borders of Europe are close at hand, marked by the east-ern limit to which European birds have spread. And as the descent is slowly made into the lower altitudes of Europe, such familiar European species as the starling, the roller and the bee eater begin to be encountered.

Here also the nature of the boundary changes. As the mountains dwindle away, their role as a great natural fence separating the Palearctic and tropical worlds is taken up by the Mediterranean trench and by the arid lands of the Sahara and the Middle East. From here to the Atlantic Ocean, the barrier is made up of water and desert.

The Mediterranean is not a sea in the sense that other seas are. It is a virtually closed basin which each year receives from the rivers and seas draining into it less water than it loses by evaporation. The cloudless skies and the almost per-petual sunshine that attract millions of European holidaymakers each summer to its shores unfortunately also have their drawback: they leave the Mediterranean with a water debit which can only be repaid by continued reinforcement from the Atlantic. But the Atlantic supply comes through an inlet, the Strait of Gibraltar, which is both narrow and shallow—in places less than eight miles wide and little more than 1,000 feet deep. Through this small channel the surface waters of the Atlantic must flow in continuously at a speed of two to three knots to make up for the loss by evaporation. If, through some geological catastrophe, this narrow door to the ocean were to be suddenly closed, the Mediterranean as we know it today would be doomed. It has been calculated that it would lose nearly 2.5 million cubic feet of water per second through evaporation. Its level would drop nearly 35 inches per year, and in less than 2,000 years the sea water it now contains—close to a million cubic miles—would have completely disappeared. Though rivers would, of course, continue to pour fresh water into its bed, enormous areas would consist of great salt flats; the wine-dark sea of Homer would be no more than a bitter, remnant puddle.

Long before the Mediterranean could dry up, however, the area would be radically transformed. As the sea retreated the shallower depths would emerge as islands, notably between Sicily and Tunisia, and divide the sea into separate western and eastern basins which would slowly get saltier and saltier just as the modern Dead Sea is doing. Deprived of the gigantic cooling plant constituted by the present sea, the vegetation of the neighboring regions would soon change dramatically. A spectacle of indescribable desolation would gradually succeed to the most agreeable of landscapes.

The fact of its being virtually a closed basin dependent entirely for survival on a narrow and shallow channel explains the two fundamental characteristics of the Mediterranean: the absence of tides and the uniform temperature of its water. Without tides, a characteristic offshore formation has developed. This is the so-called *trottoir* so familiar on the French Riviera. It consists of ledges growing out from the rocky shore, not unlike coral reefs. However, these ledges are not made of coral animals, but are built up from the remains of infinite numbers of minute plants—calcareous algae. The upper surfaces of the ledges are hard and rocklike, flush with the surface of the water; the plants that made them are long since dead. But the undersides of the ledges are very much alive. They also harbor a rich and colorful flora and fauna, the delight of skindivers and underwater naturalists. One curious denizen of the upper surface of the calcareous ledges is a small spider, *Desidiopsis*, which lives right among the splashing waves but weaves a kind of waterproof silken bell around itself. There it lives safe and dry and there it lays its eggs. Another spider, *Desis*, leads the same kind of life in coral reefs—but its home, surprisingly, is thousands of miles away in the Indian Ocean.

T HE second basic characteristic of the Mediterranean resulting from the shallowness of the Gibraltar inlet is the uniformity of water temperature throughout this sea. The raised threshold of the Atlantic doorway acts as an obstacle to the inflow of any really cold water—rich in nitrates—from the depths of the ocean. As a result, the water even at the bottom of the Mediterranean is little colder than it is at the surface. Its uniform warmth and its lack of nitrates and phosphates—the fertilizers necessary to the multiplication of all microscopic algae—explain the sea's low productivity in plankton and, in consequence, its notorious poverty of fishes and other marine life. This same lack of plankton life gives the Mediterranean its lovely azure hue, but its sar-

HOW RAINS FORM IN WINTER OVER THE MEDITERRANEAN

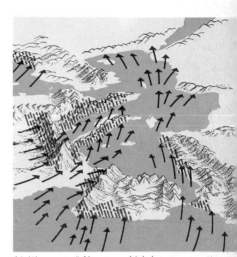

Unlike most of Europe, which has year-round precipitation, the Mediterranean lands have a climate which combines winter rains and summer drought. In winter the prevailing winds tend to blow from the north and west. When they reach the western Mediterranean basin, they are warmed and pick up moisture from the sea. Over the high mountains along the serrated coast, they rise, become chilled and drop their moisture as rain or snow. At the eastern end, where the mountains are lower, there is less rainfall; and in summer, with diminished winds and more even temperatures, condensation is less all along the coastline, resulting in the Mediterranean's famous sunny skies and notorious drought.

dines and anchovies, for instance, never attain the size they do in the Atlantic.

Finally, another factor making for poverty of marine life is the narrowness of the continental shelf—the sunny shallows which teem so richly with life in other seas. Whereas in North America or western Europe shallow water may extend for miles out to sea, it may be only a few yards in extent in the Mediterranean, or even completely absent. The deep gulfs and narrow headlands which lend such charm to parts of the Mediterranean coast often owe their capricious forms to collapses too recent in time to have allowed erosion to soften their contours or silt up the bottom. Frequently, the cliff falls sheer into the sea and continues almost straight down. Fishermen and yachtsmen trying to anchor know this well: they may find themselves in many fathoms of water only a few feet from shore. The explanation of this precipitousness is found in a long history of powerful earth movements in the Mediterranean basin, coupled with repeated volcanic cataclysms which have left their mark in the many layers of ash found in cores taken from the sea bottom.

THERE are not many vertebrates indigenous to the Mediterranean. One of the most interesting and rare is the Mediterranean monk seal, which once abounded all along the Mediterranean and Black Sea coasts and overflowed even to the northwest shores of Africa, the Canary Isles and Madeira. In former times the monk seals must have formed large colonies; the *Odyssey* tells how Ulysses, clad in the skin of a seal and mixing with a school of them, surprised Proteus, the old man with the head of a human and the tail of a fish, in order to drag a secret from him. Today, monk seals, persecuted by fishermen for more than 2,000 years, have become so rare as to be near extinction. Hardly more than a few hundred of them can be still alive. In those places where they are known for certain to have survived—Corsica, Yugoslavia and Bulgaria—they appear to breed only in rocky surf-splashed caverns which are accessible only from the sea. The largest colony today is outside the Mediterranean, on the coast of the Spanish Sahara often called the Rio de Oro.

Among sea birds, only one species is strictly Mediterranean—the Audouin's gull, recognizable by its vivid red beak with a black bar and yellow point, and feet of a somber olive green. Likewise rare and threatened by extinction, this gull nests on a few small islands—Columbretes, between the Balearics and Spain; the Chaffarines isles and the islets of the Straits of Bonifacio—on a few places along the Corsican coast and the coasts of Algeria and Tunisia, and on a few islets of the Aegean Sea.

Of some 500 species of fish that the Mediterranean can claim, about 80 are endemic, more than half being gobies and blennies. Famous in this area among invertebrates is the spectacular red coral, hunted since the days of antiquity for its scarlet gills used in jewelry.

So much for the Mediterranean as a barrier. Between it in the west and the Himalayan wall in the east lies a formidable line of desert running through the Middle East and across the Arabian peninsula and northwest Africa, completing the isolation of Palearctic Eurasia. All of Arabia and all the surrounding lands of the Persian Gulf as far as Baluchistan and the Indus valley are characterized by a landscape that is almost all desert, making an insuperable barrier to the penetration of tropical animals and plants. Palearctic Eurasia is therefore a world closed in almost completely, a kind of isolation chamber in which survive flora and fauna terribly impoverished by Pleistocene glaciations and profoundly modified, as will be seen, by the activities of man.

THROUGH MIST-HUNG GORGES, THE UPPER YANGTZE WINDS 1,500 MILES BEFORE BECOMING CHINA'S GREAT RIVER, GATEWAY TO THE SEA

Challenging the Heights

The heartland of Asia lies behind a massif of icy pinnacles and high plateaus stretching from Afghanistan to the Chinese border and forming the world's greatest barrier to weather, to the spread of plants, animals and even man. Locked in the heights, scarcely accessible even in the jet age, are regions harboring some of the rarest, least-known species, many discovered less than a century ago.

PIERCING THE PEAKS, a new highway (*above*) tunnels through the Hindù Kush mountains at nearly 11,000 feet. Recently completed, it has shortened by 120 miles the route from the U.S.S.R. to the Afghan capital of Kabul.

DEEP IN THE DESERT, at the end of an 800-mile trek, the Roy Chapman Andrews Gobi expedition of 1925 winds toward sandstone cliffs, where the naturalist found, among other things, kites nesting near fossil dinosaur eggs.

44

Central Asia: No Man's Land

Through millennia, the mountains and deserts of central Asia isolated various forms of plant and animal life behind their formidable barriers. Travelers from Europe for many centuries could only skirt this vast and unexplored area. They risked the tortuous trails through the Hindu Kush mountains to the plains of northern India and followed caravan routes westward along the fringes of the Gobi desert into China. Itself a barrier, the Gobi stretches 1,000 miles across Asia, a wasteland of salt basins and desolate scrub. Not until the end of the 19th Century could scientists and explorers, leaving caravan routes, penetrate into the interior, opening new territories for collectors in this Asian no man's land.

ROY CHAPMAN ANDREWS (SECOND FROM LEFT) POSES WITH ANTELOPES SHOT FROM CARS THAT PURSUED THEM ACROSS THE FLAT GOBI

MISSIONARY-NATURALIST Père David collected plants and found the first giant panda in western China.

RUSSIAN ZOOLOGIST Nicolai Przewalski won a major general's rank for exploration. He died trying to reach Lhasa.

PLANT COLLECTOR Joseph Rock discovered a blight-resistant chestnut tree and mapped the upper Yangtze.

PLAINS IN A SPEEDING DODGE TOURING CAR HE CLOCKED MAXIMUM SPEEDS OF ANTELOPES AT 60 AND WILD ASS AT 40 MILES PER HOUR

The Explorers

From the Victorian era through the early 1930s, the museums, parks and gardens of Europe and America received a steady flow of previously unknown exotic plants and animals from central Asia. Missionaries, consular officials and botanists hired by the East India Company were the first collectors; they were followed by "shotgun" naturalists, hunters of specimens and new species. Then came the full-scale expedition, conceived by Roy Chapman Andrews, who led five cavalcades into central Asia. The largest, in 1925, probed the natural history of the arid Gobi, at a cost of $700,000, with 40 men, eight motor cars, and 150 camels.

GERMAN EXPLORER Ernst Schäfer made an exhaustive study of the wildlife on the Tibetan plateau. From several expeditions in the 1930s, he brought back many big game animals, including the steppe bear (*above*).

47

To the Top of the World

Though collecting is a primary concern of the professional naturalists of the 20th Century, their real love has always been exploration. The British botanist Kingdon Ward was fascinated by the contrast between rain-soaked upper Burma and the drier Tibetan mountainsides. Ascending toward the crest of a divide in 1922, he looked back and saw a mist bank held back at 11,000 feet as though by some invisible barrier—actually dry air sweeping through the mountain pass. Crossing to the Tibetan side, he found conifer woods and alpine meadows. It was in these geographically close but vastly different habitats that William Beebe did much of the research for his classic monograph on the pheasants of the world. To the west, the highest peaks beckoned. Edmund Hillary, who combined a passion for mountaineering with scientific investigation, led the way up unconquerable Everest in 1953. Seven years later, scientists from five nations joined his assault on two other giants, Ama Dablam and Makalu, seeking answers to the many mysteries of the Himalayan weather, plant and animal life.

WILLIAM BEEBE pursued a wide range of zoological interests on more than 60 expeditions. Dean of the new breed of naturalist, Beebe climbed Himalayan heights and plumbed depths in the Atlantic.

KINGDON WARD collected relatively few seeds in the Himalayas, but all were taken from plants that he had seen in flower. These included 14 varieties of rhododendron which are now grown in Western gardens.

OUT OF KATMANDU and into a monsoon mist treks a line of porters supporting Sir Edmund Hillary's 1960-1961 winter expedition to the Himalayas. In all, 500 porters supplied 22 scientists probing man's adaptability to altitude. One scientist lost his legs to frostbite, others suffered strokes and pneumonia. Their conclusion: above 18,000 feet, man begins to die.

49

TIBETAN RAVEN, ABOVE 10,000 FEET

HIMALAYAN GRIFFON, ABOVE 10,000 FEET

NEPALESE AGAMID, 5,000 TO 10,000 FEET

CENTRAL ASIAN FOX, ABOVE 12,000 FEET

STRIPED BLUE CROW BUTTERFLY, SEA LEVEL TO 7,500 FEET

HIMALAYAN GRASSHOPPER, 6,000 FEET

Life in the Highest Places

Mountains manufacture their own climate. In the Himalayas a combination of great height and enormous mass has produced extremely varied living conditions. The southernmost peaks are almost drowned in snow dumped by the monsoons sweeping in from the ocean. But a little farther north, on Everest, Makalu and others, the snow-fall is lighter and much of it evaporates into the thin air. There, on the sunny slopes, life exists at higher altitudes than anywhere else on earth, and the lowland jungles creep as high as 8,000 feet.

This produces a great flexibility in Himalayan plant and animal forms, a few of which are shown in the pictures above. The striped blue crow but-

STELLARIA DECUMBENS, 20,130 FEET

ANAPHALIS, ABOVE 17,000 FEET

ALLARDIA, 14,000 TO 18,000 FEET

GENTIANS AND BUTTERCUP LEAVES, 13,000 TO 14,500 FEET

CINQUEFOIL, 11,000 TO 13,000 FEET

GIANT ARUM, 5,000 TO 9,000 FEET

terfly, found at sea level in other places, lives at altitudes of up to 7,500 feet. Higher, in the alpine zone, snow lasts only eight weeks, and flowers bloom from April (gentians) on into late October (allardias). Daily temperatures are so variable that insects fly in a tropical environment at high noon, while nocturnal mammals must forage in subfreezing midnight cold. The world's loftiest flowering plant, *Stellaria decumbens*, lives in the Himalayas, as do birds with phenomenal vertical ranges. The Tibetan raven, for example, is commonly found at 10,000 feet but it will camp-follow mountain expeditions to 25,000 feet, where it may meet the Himalayan griffon vulture soaring among the peaks.

51

15,000 FEET

10,000 FEET

8,000 FEET

6,000 FEET

3,000 FEET

A Mountainside in Szechwan

The long eastward-running walls of the Himalayas fetch up against the north-south ranges of western China. This clash of mountain systems produces a world of snow-covered sharp peaks and saw-toothed battlements thrusting up in slopes that sometimes reach 70 degrees of grade from canyons and gorges more than 20,000 feet deep. Climate and vegetation zones range from subtropical to arctic and in them a tremendous variety of animals is found. Szechwan, heart of the area, contains more than a fourth of all the animal species in China, among them some of the world's rarest.

This painting shows a landscape in the Hsifan mountains of Szechwan, emphasizing the bands of vegetation that occur at different altitudes. To its right are enlarged views of five of these bands, showing details of the vegetation, each with a characteristic animal form.

The lowest of these zones is the arid rocky slope and sparse meadow found between 3,000 and 6,000 feet and inhabited by the goral, a fleet-footed rock goat with a prominent white throat patch. Next is the thick bamboo forest, stretching from 6,000 to 8,000 feet in altitude, where the giant panda lives. The lesser panda and orange snub-nosed monkey live higher up in the dense rhododendron thickets within the 8,000-to-10,000-foot deciduous forest zone. Bulky takins, snuffling over the slopes with bulbous noses, roam widely but prefer to spend the summer in spruce and pine woods at 10,000 to 15,000 feet. Finally, herds of bharal, or blue sheep, graze the open alpine meadows from 15,000 to 18,000 feet.

53

TIBETAN GAZELLES ROAM THE SOUTHERNMOST STEPPE OF THE HIGHLANDS AT 12,000 FEET ALTITUDE AS MALES (WITH HORNS) BATTLE EACH OTHER

AT 14,000 FEET: A STEPPE BROWN BEAR AND KIANGS

Three Steppes Northward

Walled away by the mountains from the moderating influences of the oceans, the high Tibetan plateau is a vast 700,000-square-mile tableland of harsh weather, frigid gale-force winds, blistering 100-degree noontimes and bitter-cold sunsets, nights and dawns. Ernst Schäfer, the German explorer, divided it into three steppes named for the big animals most often found in each, and these are portrayed

FOR POSSESSION OF THE FEMALES. AT THE RIGHT ABOVE, A TIBETAN SAND FOX CHASES A BLACK-NOSED PIKA, ITS MOST ABUNDANT FOOD SOURCE

in the paintings on these pages. The Tibetan Gazelle Steppe (*above*) is a region of relatively rich grasslands. The Kiang Steppe (*left*), named for the Tibetan wild ass, is colder and more arid. Farther north is the Wild Yak Steppe (*right*), where shaggy yaks, walking masses of tangled hair, roam about in herds of as many as 2,000, grazing the wastes. In their search for food, they sometimes go up to 20,000 feet.

AT 15,000 FEET: WILD YAKS AND TIBETAN ANTELOPES

THE COSTA BRAVA, Spain's wild coast, rears majestically over the Mediterranean Sea. Like much of the surrounding region, shown on the map above, this salty sea is a virtual desert, its blueness an indication of a dearth of plankton.

3

Ravaged Lands on the Azure Sea

EIGHT thousand years ago the world of the Mediterranean had a vastly different aspect from the one it wears today. Where Athens now stands on its barren hills, there grew a forest of oak and pine. At Cannes, where the dry and rocky Mediterranean littoral rises steeply to the heights of the Maritime Alps, was a wilderness of evergreens and laurel. The arid wastelands of modern Iran were covered with open stands of pistachio trees; oaks and junipers flourished in the Zagros Mountains. From the gateway of the Atlantic to western Asia, the Mediterranean area, the "middle land" of our forebears, was covered with a blanket of forest which even extended to some of the land we know today as total desert along the North African coast.

What happened to these Mediterranean forests? What chain of events withered the rich flora and fauna of this part of the world that they should have changed so drastically in so relatively short a period of time?

We think of the Mediterranean today chiefly in terms of its European coastline, a place evocative of colorful landscapes bathed in brilliant light; of tiny villages cresting mountaintops whose very tints they have adopted as though they had grown from the native rock itself; of red cliffs and bare white islands

VEGETATION HIGH AND DRY

In the poor soil of the Mediterranean lands grows a variety of drought-resistant trees and vines (below and opposite). In adapting to the hot, dry summers and warm, wet winters, some, like the olive tree, have developed thin, hard-surfaced leaves to protect them against drought; others have thick outer coverings like the cork of the cork oak. The grape sends long, horizontally probing roots to seek out the scanty moisture and nutriments in the flinty soils of hillsides and mountain slopes that can support few other plants. Several of these Mediterranean mainstays have come to America: cork oak and grapevine, for example, thrive in California's Mediterranean climate.

LEBANON CEDAR

Most of the Mediterranean's tall cedars were felled long ago for their straight timber. Those remaining grow up to 220 feet high and 13 feet wide. Needlelike leaves limit evaporation, and the wood's hardness makes it practically fireproof.

HOLLY OAK

Holly oaks, also known as holm oaks, once grew in great stands in the Mediterranean forest areas. Hardy and long-lived, their leathery leaves, proof against drought and drying winds, are spiky in the young plants, but round out with age.

rising from a deep azure sea; of exotic gardens; of olive groves and dense scrub among rocky hills. What most of us do not know is that we are viewing the mineral skeleton of a landscape stripped of much of its original vegetation. Eight millennia of intensive human occupation have changed this cradle of civilization as few other places in the world have been changed by man's hand—eight millennia of deforestation, overgrazing, scrub fires and the ravages of charcoal production as man increased in numbers, developed his technology and raised the cultures that eventually conquered all the rest of the globe.

What happened to the Mediterranean can be put into a few words: a progressive increase in human activity marked by the almost total disappearance of forest; the encroaching spread of semidesert vegetation as the soil grew more and more barren; and finally desert itself, spreading outward from existing desert areas. Plato was already struck by this phenomenon 2,500 years ago. In his *Critias*, he described the effects of erosion in his native Greece:

". . . The soil which had kept breaking away from the highlands . . . keeps sliding away ceaselessly and disappearing into the deep. And, just as happens on small islands, what now remains, compared with what then existed, is like the skeleton of a sick man, all the fat and soft earth having wasted away and only the bare framework of the land being left. But at the epoch the country was unimpaired and its mountains had high, arable hills, and in place of the fields of stony soil . . . it contained plains full of rich soil; and it had much forest land in its mountains, of which there are visible signs even unto this day; for there are some mountains which now have nothing but food for bees, though they had trees not so very long ago."

The trees that Plato was speaking of were some of the drought-resistant evergreen forests of the Mediterranean basin. For the climate even then was one in which a tree gained precious advantages from long-lasting leaves with a thick cuticle—leaves which would profit from sunshine by day and resist frost at night, whose sunken stomata could reduce evaporation and preserve moisture. And although nowadays we rarely find traces of the original vegetation which was already disappearing when Plato wrote, this is the type of tree that still prevails where the Mediterranean climate combines with the proper soil to give a picture of what once was there: holly oak and strawberry tree, the green pistachio and the laurel. Forests of cork oak still grow in the western part of the Mediterranean basin, particularly in North Africa, their cracked bark affording some protection against frost and fire; in Asia Minor, beyond the range of the holly oak, are still other species of the oak family.

BUT these are islands from the past; in the main, today's vegetation is of a different order. As a result of fire, grazing and the ax, the Mediterranean oak groves have gradually degenerated into a tangled scrublike growth known as maquis. Thorny creepers bind a combination of stunted oaks, strawberry trees, myrtles and other low vegetation into an almost impenetrable thicket. In the coastal maquis, one may still find the wild olive, a shrub with spiky branches and tiny fruit. Cultivated by man from early times, it is probably the parent of the domestic olive, a tree so characteristic of the Mediterranean scene that the limit of its distribution is often taken to mark the limits of the Mediterranean climate itself.

Durable as it is, the maquis is subject to damage from repeated forest fires in the dry summers. Thus it gradually degenerates into the *garrigue*, a sparse and scrubby growth that is a prelude to bare, stony wasteland. Sometimes the *garrigue* consists mostly of cistus, small shrubs with sticky branches and leaves growing densely over wide areas made gay in springtime by myriads of red, pink, yellow or white flowers. In other cases the *garrigues* are shallow growths of fragrant plants such as thyme, rosemary, lavender, the stunted and thorny kermes oak and the dwarf palm. This kind of low heath scrub stands up to very trying conditions, for the sun burns down in summer, and evaporation is high. It is not surprising, therefore, that leaves curl up and dry out and that many bulb plants, such as asphodels, lie dormant until autumn, drawing in the meantime on their underground reserves.

ALONG with the oak forest, there are still considerable stands of conifers in the Mediterranean. The stone pine grows along the northern seaboard, notably in Italy, and the Aleppo pine, vigorous and all-invading, covers more than two million acres of the hotter, drier regions of the North African coast. In its shelter flourishes an undergrowth rich in junipers, green pistachios and thyme. In Asia Minor other pines, among them the brutta, predominate.

This is the vegetation of the low plains, plateaus and littoral slopes of the Mediterranean region. As soon as one starts to climb the mountains that dominate the seaboard or progresses inland more than a short distance, the vegetation changes. On the southern slopes of the Pyrenees in Spain, the Apennines of Italy and the Pindus range in Greece, a climb of only a few hundred feet will reveal, first of all, a mixed Mediterranean forest in which deciduous trees and temperate zone shrubs mingle with evergreens of the littoral areas. A little higher are green oaks mixed with conifers that can withstand rigorous winter temperatures as well as a climate drier in summer than that of the temperate zones. The Austrian black pine is typical in the Balkans; in Corsica the Corsican pine grows into beautiful forests 2,500 to 5,500 feet up. On the Atlas Mountains of North Africa, the magnificent tracts of Atlantic cedar found between 4,000 and 8,000 feet give us some idea of what the famous stands of the cedars of Lebanon must have been like centuries ago. Climbing still a little higher on European slopes, one sees forests of beech together with a variety of boreal animal and plant species. This is the southernmost limit of their distribution; none of them exist to the east or south of the Mediterranean. There, above the level of the cedars, the junipers and the cypresses, is a kind of alpine heathland, with low bushes of prickly plants dotted over the stony ground.

As we move inland from the coast in North Africa and Asia Minor and away from the moderating influence of the sea, the climate becomes progressively more continental: winter temperatures are lower and summer temperatures higher. It is perhaps surprising to think that in winter it can snow and freeze anywhere in this huge area of torrid desert, which runs from the interior of Morocco to Afghanistan and includes the northern Sahara, Cyrenaica, lower Egypt and Yemen. Yet the Nile has twice been known to freeze over at Cairo, once in 829 and again in 1010! Only along the coast are the winters really mild.

The causes of the deforestation that has so changed the Mediterranean scene are many and have varied with the evolution of civilizations. The earliest humans living in the Mediterranean region, as elsewhere, were primitive hunter-gatherers; the damage they did was relatively slight and spread over several thousand years. More serious were the activities of the men who followed them. These were nomadic cereal grain farmers who had succeeded in domesticating goats and sheep; they cleared forests and regularly set fire to the grazing grounds on the mountainsides at the end of summer so that when the

GRAPEVINE

Grapes have grown in the Mediterranean areas for centuries, suiting themselves to heat and lack of rain, growing in soil that is like crumbled rock. The best wine, it is said, comes from grapes low in sugar which grow in the poorest soil.

CORK OAK

Cork oaks are 20 years old before being harvested. Thereafter, they are cut every nine years. On a cork tree 40 feet tall, the cork around the trunk may be a foot thick. These trees are so well adapted that some may live up to 500 years.

OLIVE TREE

Olive groves line Mediterranean hillsides and mountain slopes, eking out a living on poor soil and economizing on water. Silvery, slender and waxy, the leaf is almost watertight. The olive itself, the fruit of the tree, is up to 65 per cent oil.

FARMLANDS SALTED AWAY

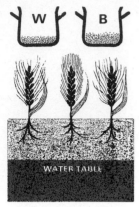

2400 B.C.

2000 B.C.

1963 A.D.

How the rich farmlands of Mesopotamia, in what is now Iraq, were ruined by irrigation with brackish water from the Tigris and Euphrates rivers is shown in the panels above. Wheat once flourished but by 2400 B.C. (top) farmers turned to barley, more tolerant of salt, as an alternate crop. Flooding, which raised the water table, increasingly salted the topsoil, and by 2000 B.C. (middle) even barley had begun to fail. Eventually the land was abandoned and the water table dropped, leaving a cropless desert saturated with salt as in the bottom panel.

autumn rains came, there would be a quick new growth of grass for their flocks.

So long as the human population remained small and dispersed, the original forest always had time to recover and to restore itself. But when the first settlements of any importance came into being, the situation changed drastically. By this time the plow had come into general use and extensive croplands were developing. The herds of goats and sheep had to be taken farther and farther away for grazing, which resulted in a permanent break between settled agriculturalists and nomadic herdsmen. Later invasions by the nomads destroyed terraces and whatever other erosion checks the farmers had devised, causing greater destruction to the land. The nomad is, in fact, not so much the son of the desert as its father.

Then too, imagine the consumption of timber necessary to a city of 20,000 to 50,000 inhabitants who needed fuel for cooking and winter heating, for firing bricks and pottery and, eventually, for smelting and treating metals. As populations spread and economic activity burgeoned, the demand for fuel became excessive and the tide of deforestation unstoppable. Nor was this all. More and more big trees were felled to provide the beams necessary for the building of great palaces, warships and commercial vessels. The mountains of Lebanon with their majestic cedars were a principal source for the timber which the Phoenicians used to build their fleets of ships, aboard which they exported still more timber to Egypt and Mesopotamia. From the same trees, Solomon procured the beams used for his temple, as did the Achaemenians for their great palace at Persepolis. In time the noble forests of Lebanon were reduced to the meager stands which today are the only remaining relics of a vanished age.

THE cutting of timber on a mountain slope means much more than the mere loss of the trees. For with the forest cover gone, the soil is exposed to the ravages of erosion. Sudden rains, instead of soaking into the well-mulched ground, now run swiftly down the slope carrying topsoil with them and making the surface stonier and more barren year by year. Meanwhile the young trees are constantly browsed down by herds of goats and never get a chance to grow big enough to replace their parents. Eventually the forest gives way to maquis—a maquis which, in its turn, is further threatened and degraded by fire and erosion. Although deforestation was one of the root causes in converting the Mediterranean region into a semidesert area, it was not the only one. There were at least two others: salinization of the soil in some of the lower lands, and the warm, dry Mediterranean climate, which does not allow vegetation to recover quickly once it has been disturbed.

The increase in the salt content of the topsoil was already evident in southern Mesopotamia when recorded history began. The Girsu documents of southern Iran, which date back 4,300 years, make mention of progressive salinization of cultivated lands, leading at first to a reduction in the sowing of wheat, only slightly tolerant to salt, in favor of the more salt-tolerant barley. As the soil became more and more salty, wheat crops disappeared completely and even the barley harvests began to fail. This crisis preceded by only a short time the collapse of the brilliant Sumerian civilization. By 1700 B.C. the center of activity in Mesopotamia was forced to move northward, where Babylon was beginning to gain in importance; the south never again recovered its former economic and political supremacy. Very much the same thing was repeated in central Iraq between 1300 and 900 B.C. and, finally, in the 13th Century of our own era, the irrigated lands in the region east of Baghdad had to be abandoned.

There are several ways in which salt gets into the soil. Initially it is produced by the breakdown of rocks in which chemicals of various kinds are locked. When rock disintegrates during the long, slow process of erosion and soil building, salts usually are freed. Dissolved in water, these find their way to streams and ponds and eventually to the sea—the main repository for all the salt that has been released from rocks during the last 4.5 billion years. In this way, the oceans are gradually becoming more and more salty. In the case of a small inland sea or one that is drying up, the salt accumulation is relatively rapid. In some extreme cases, notably the Dead Sea in Palestine and the Great Salt Lake in Utah, the salt has reached the saturation point; the water will hold no more, and large beds of nearly pure salts are deposited on the surrounding shores and flats. Modern salt mines exploit the vast accumulations of salt that have crystallized out of seas long since evaporated.

In the alluvial plain of Mesopotamia in the Near East, as in any dry area, there is a great deal of salt in the ground because rain water, or even water in the surface soil, evaporates before the salty minerals can be leached out. Therefore, any rise in the water table will lift salty water up to the surface soil. Floods which cover large areas with standing water can cause such a rise. Man has actively created such a situation for centuries by digging innumerable irrigation canals which continually silt up and overflow onto the surrounding land. Furthermore, in very hot and arid lands, the thirsty soil actually sucks up salty water from below by capillary action during the long, dry summers.

In this way a progressive salinity has impregnated the topsoil of many arid lands in the Middle East region, gradually limiting vegetation to the few plants that can tolerate salt. Only a few centuries were needed in order to transform the once-flourishing wheat fields into semideserts whose countless ruins and sand-choked canals bear witness to the splendor of the past.

Considering the continuous impoverishment of the vegetation in the Mediterranean lands during the last few thousand years, one might well believe that not much remains today of the original wildlife of the region. And indeed, if we compare the present fauna of large animals with that depicted in works of art of ancient Persia, Mesopotamia or even Greece, it is clear that a great number of species have disappeared or become perilously rare. Most visitors to the National Museum in Athens, on entering the section devoted to the treasures of Mycenae, are struck by the number of times lions are depicted. In a gold and silver inlaid dagger, hunters armed with bows and spears and protected by large shields can be seen attacking three magnificent lions with great, flowing manes. During Herodotus' time (circa 484 to 430 B.C.) these wild beasts were still to be found in the north of Greece, but a century later, by the time of Aristotle, the species was already considered rare and probably disappeared forever from Greece during the first century of our era.

FARTHER eastward, there were lions too. On bas-reliefs from the palace of Nineveh, now preserved in the Louvre and the British Museum, are depicted realistic lion hunts dating from the time of Ashurbanipal, between 669 and 626 B.C. But such hunts were probably uncommon since they were the prerogative of kings and princes; thus lions were still abundant up to the end of the 19th Century in the swampy plains bordering the Tigris and the Euphrates, as well as in the oak forests on the western slopes of the Zagros Mountains. The last lion known to have been captured in Persia was taken in 1923, south of Shiraz. In Syria, lions were still in existence in 1935 in a remote region near the sources of the Euphrates. In Palestine, however, the kingly beast has not been seen since the time of the Crusades. In North Africa, the last lions were noted in Morocco between 1911 and 1922, in Algeria and Tunisia in 1891, and in Libya and Lower Egypt in the 18th Century.

The African elephant was still in North Africa during Roman times and was well known to the Carthaginians, who domesticated it for purposes of warfare during the Punic wars. Even earlier there were Indian elephants in the Middle East. Thutmose III, the Egyptian pharaoh who conquered Syria, came across a herd of 120 head in 1464 B.C. These animals were probably the original source of the ivory trade which flourished for so long at Byblos. A small herd continued to survive in Syria on the higher Euphrates or on the Orontes up to the Ninth or Eighth Century B.C.

All the large mammals have not, however, completely disappeared from the Mediterranean. The tiger, although extremely rare, still inhabits the Iranian forests bordering the Caspian Sea. The striped hyena is somewhat more common and may be found from Morocco east to Tadzhikistan, Transcaucasia and Baluchistan. The same is true of the Asiatic jackal, which also penetrates the Balkan peninsula and has been taken as far north as Hungary. In southeastern Bulgaria, jackals were so abundant before World War II that the peasants regarded them as useful scavengers, but recent poisoning campaigns directed against wolves have brought about their almost complete extinction.

Besides these few survivors of large African or Asiatic species, the Mediterranean region is still home for several interesting ungulates, or hoofed mammals, peculiar to this part of the globe. The rarest of all—so rare that up to a few years ago it was believed to be extinct—is the Persian fallow deer. Some 30 of them were discovered in 1957 and 1958 by Werner Trense in the gallery forests of poplars, tamarisks and acacias bordering the rivers Dez and Karchez in the Khouzistan province in Iran. Larger and heavier than the European fallow deer, this magnificent animal once dwelt in large numbers in prehistoric Palestine. It was also frequently found in Mesopotamia during Ashurbanipal's time: the Nineveh bas-relief in the British Museum shows two males and two females caught in a net spread out at the forest's edge. The rare survivors seemingly owe their safety to the density of the forest screens bordering the Dez and Karchez rivers for 20 miles. In this, their last hideout, Persian fallow deer are solitary and almost exclusively nocturnal in their habits. Rutting takes place in August, and they lose their antlers in January or February.

The European fallow deer, which is now at home in the greater part of western Europe, was also originally a Mediterranean species present throughout that region from Spain to Greece. In Asia it can only be found in its wild state on the western slopes of the Taurus Mountains in Turkey and in the coastal regions of southern Asia Minor. It is a gregarious animal of diurnal habits, the sexes generally living separately in groups of various sizes, with the young accompanying their mothers. In Spain, for instance, adult males and females come together only at the close of summer, before rutting, which takes place in October. Antlers are shed in May.

The wild goat, though fortunately less rare than the Persian fallow deer, is nonetheless decreasing everywhere. The most important herds live nowadays in Turkey in the Taurus and Pontic chain, in the northern and western mountains of Iran and in the Caucasus. A few specimens may be found in some of the Mediterranean islands. There are probably fewer than a hundred survivors in

GIBRALTAR'S SHALLOW SILL

3000
6000
9000
FEET

Like the spillway of a giant dam, the shallow Strait of Gibraltar keeps Atlantic waters from mixing freely with those of the Mediterranean basin on the other side. Warm surface water can ride in from the ocean over the cold outflow from the Mediterranean deeps (see arrows), but the stone sill between Spain and Morocco blocks the deeper ocean waters. One effect of this is to restrict the plant and animal life of the Mediterranean, since the incoming surface waters do not contain sufficient nitrates and phosphates to support a flourishing growth of plankton, the first link in the marine food chain.

62

the White Mountains of western Crete and a few hundred, probably crossed with domestic goats, on the islands of Sporades and Antimilos in the Aegean Sea.

Wild goats are sociable animals. They can live on a variety of food. Although they graze now and then, they feed chiefly on leaves and branches of shrubs and trees. Extremely adaptable, they are to be found in the dense maquis along the seacoast as well as in the bare limestone rocks 6,500 feet up. In Iran the males may climb in summer as far as the snow line, between 11,500 and 14,500 feet. The wild goat is certainly the animal from which the domestic goat is sprung. Its great adaptability together with a relative lack of wildness with regard to man must have made initial taming an easy matter.

There are two types of wild sheep in the Mediterranean region: the mouflon and the Asiatic mouflon. Though two different races, they are probably of the same species, found today only in scant remnants of the former large flocks. In Corsica no more than a hundred now live in the forest reserve of Bavella—but these are enough to give a fairly accurate idea of their original way of life. In Sardinia there are a few hundred in the shooting preserve of Golfo Aranci.

Agile, graceful and expert climbers, mouflons are to Corsica what the ibexes and the chamois are to the continental mountain chains. They feed on grasses and leaves and, in the maquis especially, on fruit, flowers and the foliage of the strawberry tree. In winter they sometimes eat mistletoe; in the autumn, mushrooms. Their flocks of females and young run from four to 14 individuals. During rutting in November, the old isolated males often fight each other furiously, horn to horn, before temporarily rejoining the females. Adults and young alike take shelter in the rocks from the severe cold in winter and noonday heat in summer. During the 19th Century, the species was successfully introduced on a large scale to the European continent and is now to be found here and there from France to the Crimea and from Italy to Holland. Like the wild goat, it is very adaptable and flourishes in a forest environment and under climatic conditions markedly different from those of its native land.

The various races of the Asiatic mouflon are widely dispersed, from Anatolia and Cyprus in the west to Turkestan and Kashmir in the east. In Iran, the species is still common on the plateaus and in the mountainous massifs where the Belgian naturalist Xavier Misonne observed them as high up as 16,500 feet.

IN the Mediterranean zone of North Africa the mouflon's ecological niche is occupied by the Barbary sheep. This strange animal holds a place apart on account of the long, sweeping hair which forms a sort of pinafore on the chest of the adult male. Its horns are those of a sheep, but its other characteristics are more goatlike. The uniform russet color of its coat makes the creature almost invisible among the rocks which it frequents. Its range includes most of the mountains between Rio del Oro, Morocco and Egypt as well as many of the Saharan mountain ranges. It is found as far south as northern Chad.

The only monkey in the Mediterranean region is the Barbary ape, a grumpy and hulking species which can be easily distinguished from other members of its family, the macaques, because it is tailless and because of the rough grayish-yellow coat turning ocher on its head. Essentially terrestrial, it is to be found here and there in the craggy brushwood country of Algeria and Morocco, particularly alongside torrents. A small but famous community also lives on the Rock of Gibraltar, and there has been much discussion as to whether these are descendants of a line of European macaques or were introduced from North Africa. The number of apes on Gibraltar dwindled to three individuals in 1863, and the British, responding to a superstition that the Rock would fall into alien hands if the apes died out, ordered specimens imported from Morocco. This was done again by Winston Churchill after World War II, and the original Gibraltar colony is certainly considerably diluted by this time.

Although the Barbary ape has been known to European naturalists longer than any other monkey, its daily habits, strangely enough, have never yet been studied in detail. All that is known is that it subsists on a mixed diet of acorns, roots, fruits and insects. But the social structure of its troops, its sexual habits and means of communication are not very well known. It is thought that the young are born only in the spring, and if this is so, the Barbary ape is one of the rare higher primates adhering to a definite reproduction season.

When European bird watchers go down to the Mediterranean shores for the first time, it is generally with the secret hope of catching sight of one of those brilliantly colored birds which they associate with this part of the world—the greater flamingo of the Rhone delta, the European bee eater, or the common roller. Indeed, what visitor to the Camargue west of Marseilles has not kept an unforgettable memory of one of those massive flights of thousands of flamingos returning at evening to their nesting grounds? Seen in the solitude of those immense marshes in the slanting rays of the setting sun, their rose-colored feathers enhanced by two splashes of carmine on their wing coverts, these magnificent birds instantly make clear why the ancient Greeks called the flamingo "the bird with wings of flame."

The bee eater is at first sight less spectacular, but if the observer can catch it in a good light with binoculars, the exotic colors of its slender form literally leap into view—a brilliant green or turquoise blue on the body, a yellow throat, a brown back turning to gold on the shoulders.

As for the roller, with its large head and powerful beak, its azure blue plumage and russet back, it may not seem on first sight very worthy of note. But when it takes flight, spreading its ultramarine, black-bordered wings, even the most jaded tourist cannot fail to be impressed.

THOUGH these birds are typical of the Mediterranean region, they are actually not limited to this area alone, but are distributed in other parts of the Old World as well. By contrast, other species are more specifically Mediterranean and some of these are quite remarkable. There is, for example, a whole series of Old World warblers, among which the subalpine warbler and Rüppell's warbler are probably the most notable. The Barbary partridge is an odd little resident of the North African coast. The white-headed duck, a delightful little bird with a blue beak and upturned tail, nests around Morocco but also ranges northeastward as far as Lake Balkhash in the central Asian highlands and Mongolia; it is one of a number of birds, including the imperial eagle, which range past the Near East into central Asia and beyond.

This brings us to that extraordinary bird, the azure-winged magpie, which has the strangest distribution of all: one population lives in the south of Spain and Portugal while the other lives thousands of miles eastward in the north of China, Manchuria and Japan. Whether they were ever connected by populations living in-between, which were subsequently separated by ice age activity, is utterly unknown today, since bird skeletons do not fossilize easily. A similar enigma is posed by the Corsican nuthatch, which is limited to the pine forests of its native island, although closely related races live in northern China, Korea and Canada. Will there ever be an explanation for such strange distributions?

A LONE CEDAR OF LEBANON SPREADS ITS BOUGHS AGAINST A BACKDROP OF NAKED HILLS LONG SINCE STRIPPED OF THEIR ANCIENT FORESTS

A Lovely, Wasted Land

Few areas of the world have been more abused by man than the warm, sunny lands around the Mediterranean. With ax, livestock and fire, he has reduced forest and soil to ruin. Today, although still beautiful, the region is but a shadow of its former self, providing only here and there, as the photographs on the following pages show, wistful glimpses of its once-rich plant and animal life.

REMNANTS OF THE PAST, these Corsican pines recall the lush growth that used to cover Mediterranean slopes. Such mountain forests now take up but 30 per cent of their former range.

The Glory That Was

Man's influence on the Mediterranean region and adjacent Middle Eastern areas has been so devastating that it is almost impossible to imagine what the original flora and fauna were like. Characterized to a great extent by a rolling landscape, with dry summers and mild winters marked by heavy rains, this is an area particularly subject to erosion—a problem man recognized early but only learned to cope with when it was too late. After trees that covered the hills and grass that matted the lowlands fell victim to lumbering, pasturage and farming, practically nothing remained to keep rain from washing soil away.

Nowhere in this region is the effect of erosion more dramatically apparent than in Greece, a barren land (*opposite*) that was once green and fertile. Over the centuries a great deal of Greek soil has spilled into the sea. The thin layer that remains in most places is exhausted and lacking in humus, necessary for the absorption and retention of water. And where the soil lies deep, as in the valleys, it often consists of unproductive debris from the slopes above.

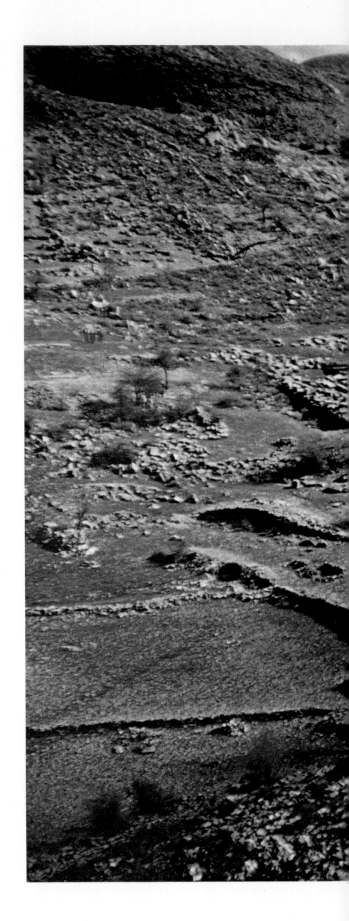

AN ISOLATED RUIN, the temple of Apollo at Bassae, Greece, stands amid rubble on a mountain slope. Mountains like these were once covered with trees, including the laurel used in the worship of Apollo, but deforestation led to the rapid erosion of the soil and exposed the underlying limestone. Today only a few hardy olive trees poke their roots between the rocks.

WILD CORK OAKS ARE PARTIALLY STRIPPED OF THEIR SPONGY BARK EVERY EIGHT TO 10 YEARS—A PROCESS THAT DOES NO HARM TO THEM

MEDITERRANEAN PLANTS ARE ADAPTED TO EXTREMES OF DEPRIVATION—EVEN, LIKE GOOSEFOOT (LOWER RIGHT), TO SALTY SOIL BAKED HARD

WEAVERS BROOM   OLEANDER   YELLOW ASPALATHUS

DESERT CANDLE   WHITE CISTUS   GOOSEFOOT

DOMESTICATED OLIVE TREES ARE SLOW-GROWING BUT EXTREMELY LONG-LIVED, SOME REPORTEDLY ACHIEVING AGES OF OVER 1,000 YEARS

A Handful of Survivors

Of all the many varieties of trees once widespread throughout the Mediterranean region, no more than a few have managed to persist in numbers anywhere close to those of the past. The trees that did were hardy enough to hang on and were also given a measure of protection because they had commercial value. Forests of cork oak cover six million acres and groves of olive trees another 10 million. Requiring little care, both types of tree show remarkable survival properties—the cork oak being able to withstand fire and frost because of its bark; the olive, droughts five to six months long. The ancient Greeks knew this and planted olive trees on their eroded, arid hillsides. Today, in areas where man's plundering has left waste unsuitable even for the olive, the ground covering, if present at all, is likely to consist of tough, drought-resistant plants like those at left.

ENCROACHING DESERT DUNES threaten a stand of date palms, familiar trees of oases. In this denuded area, with no ground cover to stay the sand, dunes advance at a rate of 40 feet a year.

69

Robbers of the Soil

Although deforestation has contributed greatly to soil erosion, heaping as much as 28 feet of silt on the ruins of Antioch alone, it is not by any means the sole agent in the destruction of the Mediterranean land. Another is overgrazing, a practice that also continues today *(below)* and robs the soil of even the meagerest of coverings. Overgrazing and intensive agriculture around the headwaters of the Tigris and Euphrates rivers in the highlands of Armenia caused such heavy erosion there that silt deposited in the Persian Gulf, 1,700 miles away, has extended the coastline of Sumerian times outward by 180 miles in 4,500 years. Inefficient farming methods have also led to erosion *(opposite)*, and many former towns in Syria now lie buried under sand and dust that once was soil on cultivated fields.

LIKE A BABYLONIAN ZIGGURAT, a wood-burning brick kiln rises from bare ground. Brickmaking, carried on for 5,000 years in the Mediterranean area, has taken a heavy toll of trees.

A HUNGRY SHEEP SCRABBLES FOR A GREEN MORSEL IN A SUN-SCORCHED DESERT IN ISRAEL, PAYING THE BITTER PRICE OF OVERGRAZING

A PRIMITIVE OX-DRAWN PLOW cuts a shallow furrow in stony ground. This Middle Eastern field, once productive, now has a low yield, its soil blasted away by winds. The villain here is the archaic "hoe" plow—it merely scratches the earth, leaving topsoil and organic matter on the surface, where the mixture pulverizes into dust and is blown away by desert winds.

A SALT FLAT TODAY, FIT ONLY FOR THE PASSAGE OF CAMELS, THIS STRETCH OF AFGHAN DESERT MAY SOON BE MADE ARABLE AGAIN. BY DIGGING

A NEW DRAINAGE CANAL alongside an old one in the Afghan desert points to a need for education as well as irrigation. Natives planted trees at the edges of—and even in—the original ditch to assure their growth in the arid climate, thereby clogging the channel with roots, making clearing by machines impossible and causing floods which brought salt to the surface.

DRAINAGE CANALS LIKE THE ONE IN THE FOREGROUND, AGRONOMISTS HOPE TO FLUSH OUT SOME OF THE SALT THAT HAS CONTAMINATED THE LAND

The Work of Reclamation

Despite the great havoc wreaked on the land by man, there is hope that some areas, seemingly beyond salvation, may yet be brought back to productivity through proper irrigation. A cause for hope is the fact that in regions of great aridity rain has not leached the valuable surface minerals from the topsoil. At the same time, however, there is concern that irrigation will raise the water table and in so doing bring increasing amounts of harmful salt to the fertile surface through capillary action, as happened in ancient times and again, only recently, in Afghanistan. Measures being taken today in Afghanistan to combat salinization include flushing the fields with water to wash out the crystallized salt, and the digging of deep drainage ditches (*above and left*) to assure that the water table will stay below a safe minimum.

FEATHERY TAMARISK TREES, shown with huts in the background, are being used to restore Afghan soil. Salt tolerant, they sop up excess water, guarding against further salinization.

73

THE NUBIAN IBEX, AN AGILE MOUNTAIN GOAT OF ISRAEL, EGYPT AND ARABIA, HAS LONG SLENDER HORNS, DEEPLY CORRUGATED IN FRONT

Hangers-on in the Mountains

Well adapted to arid lands and domesticated as far back as 6000 B.C., goats and sheep are still represented in the wild in the Mediterranean region by several mountain-dwelling species. The Barbary sheep (*opposite*) and the mouflon of Corsica and Sardinia (*below*) bear little resemblance to their farmyard cousins, being considerably more nimble and having a stiff, hairy coat instead of a fleece. Wild sheep generally wear horns that curve in a spiral; wild goats have horns that curve back and up, as in the bezoar below. The goats are the more agile, with the ibex the champion gymnast among them. Moreover, they can digest the toughest of vegetation and can live where few other animals could survive.

THE MOUFLON, A SHEEP

THE BEZOAR, A GOAT

TWO MALE BARBARY SHEEP, NATIVE TO THE ATLAS AND AURES MOUNTAINS OF NORTH AFRICA, LOCK HORNS

LIKE A SENTINEL, a Barbary ape about the size of an airedale looks out from the Rock of Gibraltar. Sheltered by the caves and brush of the Rock, a band of these monkeys has long lived there, the only primates of Europe besides man. The Barbary ape, found also in Algeria and Morocco, is more closely related to macaques living in southern Asia than to African monkeys.

EYED LIZARD

GECKO LIZARD

PAINTED DESERT VIPER

MARSH FROG

Dwellers in the Desert

Scorched by the sun, with surface temperatures climbing to 140° F., chilled at night and ripped by winds, the hot desert lands around the Mediterranean support animal life—and though not in any great magnitude, certainly in some variety, as the photographs on this page show. Among the many adaptations of such animals to their hostile environment is the ability of many to get along with little or no water. The desert lark *(right)*, for example, apparently gets enough moisture from dew and the insects and vegetation it eats to obviate its living near a water hole. The frog *(above, right)*, on the other hand, being an amphibian, must dwell in oases, where its presence, in the midst of desert, is as mysterious as that of the Barbary ape on the Rock of Gibraltar *(opposite)*. Were its ancestors carried to them by flash floods or introduced by man?

SAFE FROM THE WIND, a desert lark sits in its nest built in the shelter of a rock, with an outer wall made of pebbles and straw—an effective barricade against shifting sand and debris.

AN IMPERIAL EAGLE, STILL FOUND IN SPAIN AND GREECE, FEEDS ITS FLEDGLING IN A NEST BUILT IN THE UPPERMOST BRANCHES OF A PINE

THE BEE EATER is protected in France's Camargue, site of one of the few animal refuges in the Mediterranean area. It nests in tunnels up to six feet long which it digs in loose soil.

The Hard-pressed Birds

Birds in the Mediterranean region have long had a bitter struggle with man. Not only have their habitats been changed and destroyed, but their numbers continue to be decimated by the hunter. In Italy alone, nearly 100 million birds a year are shot, netted and birdlimed, a time-honored but illegal method involving the smearing of glue on branches. What makes this toll particularly tragic is the fact that many of these birds are northern species flying to or from their wintering grounds along the Mediterranean or in tropical Africa. Some, like finches, are shot for the simple fun of it; others wind up in corn-meal porridge or between slices of bread.

THE COMMON ROLLER, still fairly abundant in the Mediterranean region, now no longer nests in many sections of western Europe. A large, conspicuous migrant, it is easily bagged.

WILD RIDERS of the steppes, these horsemen of Turkmenistan typify the nomad culture of the limitless grassland and semidesert regions found in the heart of Eurasia (*see map above*). Here, the horse, friend and status symbol, is everything.

4

The Steppe Corridor

ONE of the dominant features of Palearctic Eurasia is a vast, often treeless zone situated in the center of the continent and extending almost without interruption from Hungary to Mongolia and northeast China. This is what historians have justly named "the steppe corridor." It was over these immense prairies and deserts that the Mongol cavalry of Genghis Khan thundered, the caravan of Marco Polo made its way, and centuries of trade flowed between the Mediterranean world and China. And over them also, imperceptibly but ceaselessly, went on the interchange of genes, of technologies and religions.

What makes the steppe corridor a natural line of communication between East and West is not merely that it is relatively flat with few mountain barriers, but also that it is open country. This is not the result of man's activity, as in so many other parts of the world, but of the climate, which is determined by the very vastness of Eurasia. As one advances inland from the sea for hundreds, and eventually thousands of miles, the air becomes steadily drier, the rainfall scantier, and the differences between winter and summer temperatures increase. The outer portions of this zone are forest steppe, which gives way to prairie. Further inland is the semidesert steppe, and finally the desert.

The prairies of southern Russia and western Siberia have a black soil rich in organic matter—the famous chernozem. Out of this deep and fruitful earth grow many tufted grasses—principally fescue, koeleria and, most abundant of all, many varieties of feather grasses. Flowers bloom too, their bright colors from time to time briefly lighting up a landscape that is normally monotonous and drab. There are wild red and yellow tulips, yellow and bluish-violet steppe irises, dark red peonies, purple hyacinths, blue sage and many more. As for the grasses, these rarely flower before May, but then the scene becomes an extraordinary one: the plain is covered with a carpet of silvery gray which undulates with the breeze like the billowing surface of the ocean. This is truly the "sea of grass" of which early travelers in this limitless land spoke with awe.

When they are full-grown the grasses hide all other plants except the steppe thistles, whose large red heads alone break the monotony of the prairie. Then comes the summer drought, the grass turns yellow and the whole vast land looks like an immense coconut matting, covered as it is by the dried-up stalks of the feather grasses, which serve as fertilizer for the next year's growth.

The closer one approaches the center of the continent, the poorer the soil becomes and the larger the patches of bare ground between the tufts of vegetation. Here is the semidesert steppe, and it is aptly named. Prairie grasses still grow, particularly fescue and the feather grasses, but the tufts are fewer and shorter as the climate grows more severe. Sagebrushes, however, thrive in such conditions, and their bitter fragrance impregnates the air of the steppe. When it rains in the spring, short-lived annuals bloom, such as tulips, buttercups and a rhubarb known locally as "camel's grass." In the Astrakhan region, where the Volga flows into the Caspian Sea, the open ground between the tufts of sagebrush is carpeted by a moss so black that one would think the earth had been scorched. Beyond the Urals, these moss patches give way to a "crust" of lichens.

DEEPER yet, in the very heart of the continent, is the true desert, its boundaries enclosing an area where the rainfall is less than six inches a year. But this is not quite the scorching desert of popular conception. True, it is hot enough in summer, with temperatures of over 100°F. a commonplace. But in winter it is bitterly cold, giving this region the greatest extremes of temperature found anywhere else on earth. It points up the picturesque description once given to the climate of central Asia: "In summer, eggs boil; in winter, water freezes." Snow lies for an average of 37 days at Tashkent and 70 days at Novo-Kazalinsk. Under these conditions it is not surprising that the vegetation is thinly spread, although by the standards of the Sahara or Arabia it is still abundant. Where the soil is not too poor, sagebrush and saltbush grow. Where sand prevails, one finds the white saxaul; where it turns salty, the black saxaul.

The saxauls are among the strangest of the desert plants of central Asia. They are bushes which grow in almost impenetrable thickets up to 20 or more feet high, but whose branches show only the tiniest of leaves, sometimes even none at all. The naturalist V. N. Chnitnikov once wrote of them: "The impression on anyone not accustomed to the sight of a forest of saxauls is almost terrifying. First of all, despite its density it has the air of being, as it were, quite white, because the light bark of its trunks and the constitution of its branches create no shade. In the heat, it is more suffocating there than elsewhere because it keeps out the wind but offers scant protection against the sun. What is more, an almost perpetual silence reigns there because the feathered world is represented neither by many species nor by many individual birds."

In the sandy wastes of Kara Kum in Soviet Central Asia, the principal settled plant is three-awn grass, a plant whose buds, when covered by the shifting sand, throw out underground creeper stems, or rhizomes, from which new stems grow to the surface. Its companion, the *dzhuzgun* shrub, has mainly horizontal roots which sometimes attain a length of over a hundred feet.

Inhabiting the tremendous reaches of steppeland in Eurasia is a remarkable array of herbivorous mammals. Social in habit, they are for the most part also long-range wanderers. Both traits are advantageous to big, grazing ungulates. Erratic rainfall, periodic drought and winter snows prevent any kind of sedentary existence for these larger animals. To sustain a sedentary life at all, they would have to be so thinly distributed that it would be very difficult, if not impossible, for them to meet for purposes of reproducing, thus jeopardizing the future of the species. The reproduction problem is solved if the animals live as a herd, but then the herd must keep moving all the time to find food. In areas where rainfall follows a regular rhythm, these migrations may be regular as well, but where rain comes only sporadically, the animals are forced into endless wandering, and prolonged droughts and hard winters take a heavy toll.

FEATHER GRASS

Blanketing the vast steppes of the Asian heartland, feather grass, or needle grass (above), holds the soil in place with its shallow roots much as it did on America's Midwestern prairie. The "feathers" are actually threads, attached to the seeds. Saxaul (below), a small hardwood shrub, is well adapted to life in the Asian deserts; its juicy bark is a water reservoir. To prevent evaporation, white saxaul grows only small, narrow leaves; black saxaul leaves are merely tiny scales. In winter both types shed their branches, to grow new ones in the spring.

THE steppe seems for a long time to have been the favorite habitat of the wild horse and wild ass. The best known of all—probably extinct now in its wild state—is Przewalski's horse, named for the great Russian naturalist and explorer of central Asia. This is a small animal about four feet in height, not much bigger than a large donkey but with relatively heavier limbs and a proportionately bigger head. The pale summer coat is reddish brown on top, turning lighter on the flanks to become yellowish white on the belly. In winter, the hair grows longer and thicker, and turns lighter.

The horses formerly lived in troops of five to 11 head led by a stallion who did not leave the females except during the short period of foaling between the end of April and the beginning of May. These animals are vigorous and, for horses, aggressive. At rutting time, the adult males often fought each other in desperate combat. Sometimes they even raided Mongolian nomad camps, killing off the stallions and bearing away the domesticated mares, which suggests that the last troops of Przewalski's horse may not have been as free from crossbreeding as was previously assumed.

The diet of these robust creatures must have been very Spartan when we take into account the character of their last refuge in the semidesert regions to which they were driven. They ate whatever grasses managed to subsist in these inhospitable places, and also sagebrush, wild bulbs and halophytes. In winter and spring, water presented no problem: Przewalski's horse ate snow or drank from thawing pools. In summer, on the other hand, the presence of drinking places accessible every second or third day was a *sine qua non* of their survival, as these animals could not go more than four days without water.

WHITE SAXAUL

During the last half century, Przewalski's horse became increasingly rare. In Prague in 1961, Andrei G. Bannikov of Moscow University pointed out that no one had seen it in Mongolia for more than five years. An expedition sent by the Peking Zoo in 1955 to 1957 into the Baytag Bogdo mountains and Takhin Shar Nuru ("the range of the yellow wild horse," in the Mongol tongue), where the horse was still common in 1950, failed to capture a single specimen.

This sudden and final disappearance in less than a decade is extremely puzzling. It was presumably caused by the spread of nomadic herdsmen into the region. Frightened away from the few available drinking places by the continual presence of sheep flocks, the last small bands probably died of thirst. The future of Przewalski's horse rests today on a small population of some 80 head surviving in various zoological gardens. International efforts are now being made to raise, from this hard core of survivors, a stock large enough to reintroduce the species eventually into a national park or sanctuary.

THE Asiatic wild ass exists in several forms. Happily, most of these are not as immediately menaced as the wild horse, but even their future prospects are grim enough over the greater part of the area where they are still to be found. A little smaller than Przewalski's horse, the kulan, or Mongolian wild ass, is distinguishable from it by its finer head and by a handsome tail ending in a brush of long, black hair. Its winter coat is gray, but in summer it turns a reddish color. Farther to the south, the onager, or Persian variety, is distinguishable from the kulan by being somewhat smaller and having longer ears and not so luxuriant a tail. Another form, with a light fawn coat and black mane, which formerly inhabited Syria, Mesopotamia and northern Arabia, has now completely disappeared.

The living space of the Mongolian wild ass has been diminishing steadily for the last 2,000 years. Around 200 B.C. the species bred abundantly in Europe in the region of Odessa and persisted in the province of Kiev as late as the 12th Century A.D. Six hundred years later, there were still kulans in Europe on the west bank of the river Volga—while in Asia they could be found over a wider area extending north as far as latitude 50°, along the upper reaches of the Amur river. Today the range of these animals has shrunk to a small section in central Mongolia. The Persian form is even more restricted. It persists only in the Badkhyz game reserve in Turkmenistan and in northeastern Iran.

The kulan, like Przewalski's horse, is an animal of the steppeland rather than the true desert. It cannot get sufficient water by eating plants, but must drink

ROUTES FOR WAR AND TRAVEL

Conquering warriors and world travelers crossed Eurasia on routes indicated by arrows on the map below. The steppes (gray areas) made fine highways for two major invasions of Europe from Asia. The Huns spread terror through France and Italy in the Fifth Century. Later the Mongols under Ogedei, son of Genghis Khan, plundered eastern Europe. The two 13th Century journeys by the Polo family of Venice revealed to Europeans such marvels as paper money, fireproof cloth (asbestos) and nuts the size of footballs (coconuts). It took many years and voyages by other travelers before people believed any of Marco Polo's tales.

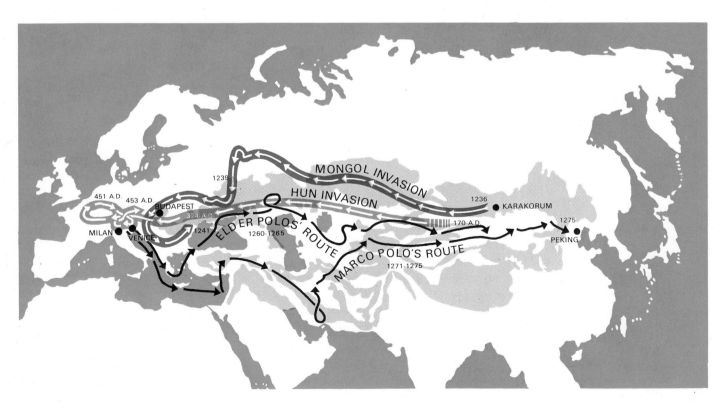

regularly, at least in summer when plants are dry. Bannikov has remarked that in warm weather the Asiatic wild ass normally drinks twice daily, at dawn and twilight, although if need be it can go without water for two or three days. Access to a permanent source of water is, then, an essential condition for the survival of the species, and in summer the kulan never goes more than nine miles from a drinking place. In winter, on the other hand, when water is plentiful but pastures leaner, the radius for roaming becomes five to six times greater.

By nature, the wild asses are all very sociable. In summer and at the beginning of autumn, they usually band together in small groups of from three to 15 head—a single stallion accompanied by females and their young. In winter, these family groups unite to form large herds of up to a thousand head. At rutting time the sociability of the wild asses ceases. The young males leave the herd to go in search of females or to join in small bands of their own, a habit which can lead to serious fights. When the mares are in heat, the stallion takes to galloping round his harem, throwing himself on the ground, rolling over on his back and braying. Rutting times vary: in Badkhyz it is the end of February or the beginning of March; in Mongolia from June to September. The young are foaled in the spring after a gestation period of about 12 months.

Besides having the stamina of true nomads, the kulans are remarkably fleet. During the Central Asiatic Expeditions for the American Museum of Natural History in the 1920s, Roy Chapman Andrews tested their speed and endurance powers. He chased a group of kulans by automobile for 16 miles, hitting speeds of up to 40 miles an hour. One stallion maintained an average speed of 30 miles an hour over the entire distance.

I F Przewalski's horse in its wild state has truly disappeared from the Mongolian steppes, then the rarest ungulate still running wild in central Asia now is certainly the Bactrian camel, the probable ancestor of the domesticated two-humped camel. The origin of these beasts is not clear: no one knows whether they are true wild camels or simply domestic camels gone wild. In a few instances where wild males have mated with domestic females, the resulting hybrids are very timid and difficult to tame, which seems to indicate that there is some genetic difference between the wild and domesticated strains.

Up to about 1920, the wild camel could be met anywhere in the Gobi desert. Since then, the survivors have been split up into two small colonies. One of them frequents the high, undulating plains between 4,800 and 6,400 feet in the Ederengin Nuru mountain chain of southwestern Mongolia, the other in northwestern China between lakes Lob Nor and Bagrach Kol.

Like the kulan and Przewalski's horse, the wild camel does not belong to the desert but to the steppe, and its resistance to drought is less than that of the true desert dromedary. When the green plants and shrubs on which it feeds begin to turn dry, it can still eat them, but then it must drink every four or five days. With the coming of autumn, it quits the open country to seek out the dried-up beds of temporary streams, where it manages to survive on the dead leaves of the native poplars. These animals live in small groups of from five to 12 head, including at least one male leader. At rutting time, which takes place in February, the males fight among themselves and chase away the youngest ones, which explains why one occasionally comes across isolated males. Foaling is in March, 13 months later.

The most interesting ungulate of the steppes is, without any doubt, the saiga, the northernmost of all antelopes. An odd-looking animal with a prom-

The Mongol emperor Temuchin (above) is known today by his title Genghis Khan, or "All-Encompassing Lord." No genuine portrait of the Khan is known, but this traditional one was for many years in the royal museum in Peking, China.

After 20 years in the Mongol Empire, Marco Polo returned by sea with an imperial mission as far as Persia. The edge of this 15th Century German woodcut reads: "This is the noble knight Marco Polo of Venice, the greatest traveler."

85

inent, mooselike snout, the saiga wears a yellow-brown coat in summer which turns grayish in winter. The male has short amber-yellow horns somewhat in the form of a lyre. Two centuries ago, the saiga could be found almost anywhere on the steppes of Eurasia. But from the beginning of the 19th Century its range steadily decreased as firearms became more widespread.

In 1919 Soviet naturalists succeeded in having the hunting of the saiga banned, but nonetheless between 1920 and 1930 the situation in which the animal found itself was tragic. Wolves and poachers preyed on it, and by 1930 there remained only a few hundred individuals. The future of this strange animal seemed desperate, much more so than that of the wild horse or ass. But after the first chaotic decade of the Russian Revolution had given way to a more stable situation, the ban on hunting the saiga became at last increasingly effective, and the saiga increased its numbers at an unexpected, even sensational, rate. Today, it has become the most plentiful of the wild ungulates to be found in the Russian steppe, its numbers reaching some two and a half million head spread over an area of almost a million square miles.

It is rare for any species of large mammal to show such a spectacular renaissance, and for a long time scientists wondered about the reason for it. A serious ecological study of the saiga undertaken during the last 10 years by Bannikov and his co-workers has now given at least a partial answer. This antelope of the steppe, to compensate for the heavy losses imposed on it every winter by an extremely rigorous climate, is gifted with a fertility equaled by few other large mammals. This fertility has several contributing causes, the most obvious being a remarkably early sexual maturity among the females. Although the male has to attain the age of 20 months before it can mate, the female of the species is ready at about seven months and can bring her first young into the world when she is herself only a year old, even before her skeletal growth is complete. Furthermore, whereas most hoofed animals give birth to only one offspring at a time, the female saiga has twins 65 per cent of the time. Finally, the habits of the antelope make certain, in a brutal but effective fashion, that the available food supply goes to those who propagate the species—the females. As with most other ungulates, as many males as females are born, but since the male antelope is polygamous and one will lord it over a harem of from five to 50 females, this means that the other males are superfluous—not needed for the propagation of the species—and most of them are weeded out as a result of the battles and fasts that they subject themselves to during the rutting season. Their struggles at this time weaken them so much that 80 to 90 per cent of them die on the snow-covered plains, leaving only as many as are needed to fertilize the females in the ensuing season.

THE saiga's reproductive activities are remarkably regular and synchronized. Most couplings take place over a 10-day period in December in the region west of the lower Volga, a little later in Kazakhstan and Mongolia. The young are almost all foaled within a six or seven days' span—at the end of April near the lower Volga, in mid-May in eastern Kazakhstan and at the end of May in Mongolia. As their time comes near, the great majority of expecting females congregates on what appears to be traditional foaling sites, open sagebrush steppes or salt semideserts far from human dwellings. As soon as the young are capable of following, at the most 10 days, they move off from these nurseries.

To these powers of growth and reproduction must be added great strength and endurance, which give the saiga exceptional mobility. This enables it to exploit pastures far distant from each other, to move out of excessively arid areas in summer and to avoid places where the snow is more than a foot deep in winter. In their migrations the herds have been observed to cover as much as 150 miles in a week.

But despite its remarkable adaptations, the saiga is like most other species described in this chapter in that it is not a desert animal and cannot wander far from accessible water during times of prolonged drought. It must drink almost every day, so that in the final analysis the presence of permanent drinking places determines whether it survives or not.

INTERESTING as the large steppe mammals are, it is not they that are the chief consumers of the vegetable growth in the "sea of grass." Far less spectacular species, present in much greater numbers, are responsible. These are the rodents, of which certain kinds that live in large colonies are particularly important. In years when they are plentiful, an average of 325,000 susliks, or ground squirrels, and voles have been estimated for every four square miles or so in some of the steppelands beyond the Volga—as against only four saiga antelopes. While the four antelopes eat about 40 pounds of green plants a day, the rodents eat two tons of grasses, bulbs and tubers. Of course, such a consumption is true only of the spring and early summer, for susliks become torpid in very hot or very cold weather and do not eat at all, and in winter voles are scarcer. Colonial rodents like these two account for about half of the species of rodents living in the Eurasian steppes and for a third of all mammal species in this region; they are definitely the predominant group of plant-eating vertebrates.

Like the prairie dogs and gophers of the American Great Plains, the burrowing rodents of central Eurasia play an important role in the natural economy of the steppes by constantly turning up the ground. The bobac marmot in particular and the 13 species of susliks are most active here; less numerous but still important are those strange subterranean rodents known as the northern mole-vole and the Russian mole rat.

The tunnels of the bobac marmot are deep and far-reaching. A single animal may dig 200 feet of passages, all leading to a nest chamber about three feet wide and located anywhere from six to 14 feet below the surface of the ground. Excavation work of this magnitude requires the bringing up of soil from far below the surface at the rate of three to six cubic feet per animal per year. It is no wonder that each colony shows its presence by a mound that is sometimes 25 to 50 feet high. Large colonies may have from 50 to several hundred burrows, each burrow the home for as many as 15 marmots. Thus the amount of earth brought to the surface from the deeper soil layers all over the steppe corridor is enormous.

The warrens of the susliks are smaller, not as long and slightly less deep than those of the bobac marmot, but they are by no means negligible. Each set of burrows, furthermore, is generally used and reused by several generations of animals, which repair and modify them continually.

All this serves to explain why some Russian soil scientists look on colonial rodents as an essential factor in preserving the vitality of the soil in prairies and steppes. By bringing to the surface earth whose composition generally differs from that on top, marmots and susliks help to diversify the vegetation. In the black-earthed prairies, for instance, the light soil carried up by the bobac marmots is rich in calcium carbonates, and the seeds of calcium-loving plants, left there in bird droppings, are able to thrive in this favorable milieu.

EXCAVATOR OF THE STEPPE

The bobac marmot digs out a network of burrows, which sometimes extends over a 500-square-foot area. It then piles up subsoil in a mound up to four feet high and 12 feet wide. Sleeping chambers, seen in cutaway view, are lined with soft grasses. A careful housekeeper, the marmot cleans its burrow each spring, pushing dirt, old bedding and other debris to the surface. These excavations bring up soils which alter the chemistry of the mound and make possible the growth of plants which otherwise would not appear there. Shown above are three of these: a variety of feather grass (at top of mound), fescue, one of the marmot's favorite foods (at left center), and ferula, similar to Queen Anne's lace (right foreground).

In the more arid southern steppes the soil carried up from below is much saltier than the surface layer, with the result that salt-tolerant plants habitually grow there. Of course the earth in mounds made by marmots or susliks changes with time, and the vegetation of old mounds is not the same as that found on the most recent ones; but as new warrens are being built all the time, earth from underground is constantly being brought up to the surface, and the vegetation of uncultivated steppes is definitely richer than it would be without the teeming presence of these indefatigable diggers.

While the rodents toil in their own fashion, much of the surrounding landscape is being more quickly and more radically changed by the efficient machinery of man. The continuous colonization of the steppe by Russians is now drastically modifying conditions which have existed in a balanced fashion for thousands of years. Starting from the southern Ukraine, the ground has been progressively cleared during the past century as far as the region of the lower Volga and the foothills of the Caucasus, and finally to Kazakhstan, southern Siberia and the steppes of the Altai mountains. The plough has already driven mole-voles and mole rats away from the regions situated on the west bank of the Volga. The bobac marmot, too, is noticeably diminishing throughout the whole of the European part of the Russian steppe.

In other places the rodents are increasing as a result of man's activity. Overgrazing by cattle, sheep and goats has modified the original vegetation of vast steppe areas; edible grasses have been replaced by sagebrush and other plants unsuitable for consumption by domestic animals. This has proved favorable to the little susliks and to certain jerboas—the great jerboa, for instance, whose European habitat has become more widespread since the beginning of the century. Only the future can say what long-term effects these changes will have on the fertility of the soil in the steppe, but there are ecologists in Russia today who believe that a complete elimination of colonial rodents would—in certain places at least—very likely result in the impoverishment of the soil.

AMONG the birds of the steppe and prairie can be found the two characteristics already so noticeable among the mammals of those regions: a tendency to swift movement while on the ground, and gregariousness. Bustards, for example, get around much more by walking and running than by flying. Only in rare instances do they take off in slow, heavy flight. This is particularly true of the great bustard, a huge bird which, in the adult male, may exceed three and a half feet in height and weigh over 30 pounds. Bustards are polygamous, and at the beginning of the breeding season the males go in for bizarre parades during which they enhance their size and appearance by turning their wings almost inside out, giving them the look of huge white chrysanthemums. Bands of great bustards generally spend the day striding ceaselessly across the steppe in search of seeds, insects and occasional small vertebrates. During recent centuries the species was widely distributed throughout the plains of western Europe, where there was an intense cultivation of cereals; today, however, they are no longer to be found there (except in Spain and the north of Germany); hunters and mechanical harvesters have driven them away.

The little bustard is also gregarious and a great walker. It is less than half the size of its large cousin and correspondingly less conspicuous. Whether or not this has had anything to do with its survival, it has held out considerably better on the European plains than the great bustard, and a few individuals are still to be found nesting in France.

Gregariousness is also a well-developed trait among a whole series of other birds of the Eurasian steppe. The demoiselle crane, whose black breast and white crest contrast so elegantly with the rest of its gray plumage, lives in flocks striking in size and appearance. The sandgrouses, which look like pigeons but have long pointed wings and tails, form large colonies, as does the sociable plover. But the rose-colored starling is probably the most gregarious of them all. This magnificent pink bird, with shining black head, wings and tail, always lives and breeds in large groups. It nests only in extensive colonies comprising as many as 7,000 pairs and at least in one instance 15,000 pairs. But what gives this starling its unique character is the fact that it is a perpetual nomad. The species nests no more than three consecutive years in the same place. It seems to follow its favorite food—locusts and grasshoppers—and seeks at the same time rocky hills, old walls or heaps of stones suitable for nest-building. The nesting season is over and done with in five or six weeks and the bands fly off to winter, mainly in northwestern India.

ONE of the strangest features of the western part of the steppe is the existence of three seas, each with very special physical characteristics and with its own flora and fauna: the Black Sea, the Caspian Sea and the Aral Sea. These three large water masses are mere vestiges of a much greater sea whose vicissitudes during Cenozoic times make an extraordinary story.

Twenty-five million years ago, at the outset of the Miocene, the combined basins of what are now the Black Sea and Caspian Sea formed a single vast stretch of salt water, an aftermath of the vanishing Tethys. The fauna was of the Mediterranean type. Not long after, communication with the Mediterranean was cut off and a closed basin was formed, the Sarmatian Basin. With no further salt water connection and with many large rivers draining into it, its surface waters became increasingly fresh. As the salt content of the water decreased, a whole series of purely marine groups, such as sea urchins, numerous shellfish, cods, dolphins and whales—disappeared and the Sarmatian fauna gradually changed for the most part to an animal population typical of brackish water.

At its largest, this immense lagoon stretched from Hungary to the trans-Caspian region, covering a sizable portion of what is now southern Russia. But the waters were not long in receding, becoming fresher as they did so, and the Sarmatian fauna took refuge in a few brackish lagoons. As the sea continued to shrink, and with the rise of the Caucasus mountains, the eastern and western parts of the basin separated, forming two seas—the Caspian and Aral on one side and the Black Sea on the other. By the end of the Tertiary the Black Sea had roughly its present size and form.

Since then, the salt content of the Black Sea has changed several times, increasing and decreasing with climatic variations. During glacial onsets, its waters have had a tendency to grow sweeter because communication with the Mediterranean has been interrupted, whereas during interglacial periods they have become saltier when the seas have risen and a connection once again established. The Caspian and the Aral, by contrast, were almost completely isolated from this time on and have slowly continued to grow sweeter.

The moral of this history is that the three "seas" we are speaking of hardly deserve that name. The modern Black Sea is only slightly salty (19 parts per thousand) on the surface. Its deep waters are very poor in oxygen, but rich in hydrogen sulphide produced by the sulphate-reducing bacteria on the bottom. The result is that all life except that of anaerobic bacteria is impossible below

A SHRINKING SEA

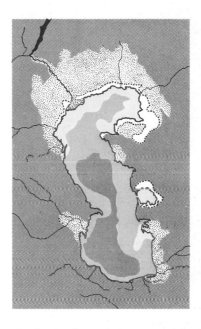

The Caspian Sea is the largest salt lake in the world (150,000 square miles) and has been alternately shrinking and growing for hundreds of thousands of years. It is now in a contracting phase. In this map the stippled area is below sea level and was presumably once under water. The small white areas next to the blue show parts of the sea that have dried up since 1889, when the current shrinkage began. If the water level were to drop another 20 feet, the lightest blue area would be dry. The darker blue tones indicate depths up to 600 feet and over 600 feet.

a depth of about 600 feet. Because of this, the waters and the bottom of the Black Sea are very largely sterile, the upper layers alone sustaining life. Its fauna as a consequence is greatly impoverished and productivity is very low. The Mediterranean shelters 1,457 species of shellfish, 251 decapods, 100 echinoderms and 549 fishes, whereas the Black Sea has only 125 species of shellfish, 35 decapods, two echinoderms and 180 fishes.

The Sea of Azov, though it looks like a northern appendage to the Black Sea, is actually more than that. Its waters, for one thing, are much fresher, and because of its shallowness—its maximum depth is about 40 feet—they undergo considerable temperature changes according to season. A certain number of invertebrates, remainders of the original Sarmatian fauna, have taken refuge in it, as they have done in other estuaries of the Black Sea. But the most important characteristic of the Sea of Azov is its enormous biological productivity, making it a very worthwhile fishing ground. The yield of fish is about 250,000 tons a year, as compared with some 43,000 tons from the Black Sea.

THE Caspian Sea in many respects is more like an unusual sort of lake— the largest lake in the world, in fact—than a true sea. Its average salt content is only about a third of that found in the oceans, and its northern part, because of the huge influx of the Volga, is almost completely fresh. Below about 600 feet its oxygen content is slight, and hydrogen sulphide is present, just as in the Black Sea, so that there can be no life in the depths. Also, the present sea level of the Caspian is more than 90 feet below the mean level of the other seas around the world. In the last 20 years it has fluctuated, since additions of fresh water from rivers and rainfall do not always compensate for loss by evaporation.

The fauna of the Caspian is fascinating. Several important marine groups— crabs, squids, sea stars, sea urchins, tunicates, sharks, whales and dolphins— are entirely lacking, but these are balanced by large numbers of species that are found nowhere else. Two thirds of its crustaceans and fishes, and four fifths of its shellfish are unique to the Caspian. Most are relics of ancient Sarmatian fauna, but a few immigrants such as the Caspian seal, closely related to the ringed seal, and the Siberian whitefish are of Arctic origin. Since 1936, Russian biologists have introduced several alien species to increase the sea's biological productivity. Among them the worm *Nereis succinea* has been particularly successful. In less than 10 years it has settled in more than 10,000 square miles and is now heavily fed upon by sturgeons and other fish.

Because of this great variety of marine life, the Caspian is a haven for a considerable variety of birds that come there to spend the winter. They can be found chiefly in the marshes, lagoons and along the beaches of the southern coast of the Caspian. Among them are flamingoes, herons and pelicans.

As for the Aral Sea, the fourth largest landlocked body of water in the world, its waters are almost fresh, like the Caspian Sea, and very shallow, its greatest depth being only about 200 feet. Its fauna is poor both in terms of species and numbers. Only 20 different kinds of fish live in its waters, all fresh-water types.

The Black Sea, the Caspian and the Aral may be little more than lakes today by comparison with the enormous body of salt water which originally gave them birth, but in their remarkable history and their present, sometimes paradoxical qualities, they reflect the character of the region in which they lie, the great plains and deserts in the heart of the Eurasian continent. How very different another part of the continent can be will be seen in the next chapter when we enter the very opposite to the steppe region, the land of leafy forests.

ON THE PRAIRIE STEPPE, WHERE THICK SOD OFTEN HOLDS MOISTURE THROUGH SUMMER DROUGHT, SHEEP MAY GRAZE THE YEAR AROUND

The Nomad's Arid Land

Cut off by high mountains from the water-laden ocean winds, the heartland of Eurasia gets little rain. Where some does fall, the land is covered by a rolling carpet of grass, the prairie steppe. Where none falls is desert. Between these extremes lie trackless regions where sparse grasses provide only seasonal pasturage, forcing nomad tribes to shuttle their flocks to and fro ceaselessly.

RAISING A PUFF OF DUST FROM THE DRY GROUND, A LONE HORSEMAN WATCHES HIS FLOCK GRAZE ON THE SCANT GRASS OF THE SEMIDESERT.

The Cruel Climate of Hunger

On the fringes of the prairie steppe, where the "sea of grass" gives way to the scattered covering of the last hardy plants that can survive, life is in constant, precarious balance between extremes of climate. There the line between semidesert and desert is scarcely perceptible, fluctuating from year to year as well as with the changing seasons. What may be good pasture in spring, watered by melting mountain snows and brief rains, will dry up completely in the torrid summers, leaving scarcely more

WHETHER IN PERSIA OR MONGOLIA, THESE EMPTY PLAINS IMPOSE A CHANGELESS PATTERN. CONSTANT MOVEMENT IN SEARCH OF FOOD

signs of life than a few brittle, yellow stalks. By then, the grazing herds will have moved on north or up into the mountains. In the fall they will return, driven by the fierce cold of winter which, unmitigated by any ocean, comes on with a frigid blast. Even the change from day to night will often be as much as 50 degrees. It is these conditions that make for nomadism. Dependent on its flocks, the human population of the steppe must move as they move in their endless effort to find food.

AN AGED QASHQAI SHEPHERD drives his flock over the last pass before reaching a summer pasture high in the mountains of central Iran, ending a 200-mile trek which had begun a month or so earlier in the lowlands near the Persian Gulf.

SUMMER HOMES of the Qashqai are mobile tent-villages in the mountains. The tribe's rulers, the Khans, control some 40,000 families and conduct all their tribal business from the large black tent in the center of the picture.

Relative Abundance in the Mountains

Where desert and mountain meet throughout much of southwest Asia, a form of nomadism exists that is quite different from that on the central plains. In winter, tribes keep their herds in the warmer foot-hills or on the sands, where rain revives the dry autumn grasses. In spring, they move up into the mountains to grasslands nourished by melting snows. This trek between seasonal pastures is a short trip compared with the constant movement of nomads on the flat plains.

Unlike those self-sufficient herdsmen to the north and east, the nomads of the southwest produce few

94

of their own artifacts, trading instead with the established agrarian communities through which they travel. In return for clothing, grain and industrial products, they offer the raw materials of their flocks —meat, hides and wool, even the manure that their animals drop as they graze in the fallow and harvested fields along the migration route. A vigorous people, the nomads often in the past took what they wanted if they could not strike a bargain, and to this day the wealthier tribes, like the Qashqai of Iran shown above, maintain a somewhat belligerent independence from the central governments.

A Mobile Life on the Plains

By contrast to the tribes which migrate between lowland and mountain, the nomads of the plains are eternally on the move and have adapted their lives, their customs and their dwellings to a wandering existence. The nomads of Mongolia, in particular, have evolved through centuries a portable house so practical that it is now mass-produced in factories. Called the yurt, this collapsible, one-room structure can be assembled in less than half an hour. The skeleton of a yurt consists of a wooden frame which supports a dome of spokes gathered at a central ring. This ring, left uncovered, serves as a vent for the fire, placed in a pit or stove directly beneath it. Over the wooden frame a number of layers of felt are tied, as many as eight during the winter, when temperatures may drop to −35° F., and as few as one during the heat of summer. On top of the felt a protective canvas is usually stretched which helps keep off the rain. But it is against the winds which blow unchecked across miles of undulating plain that the yurt is particularly resistant: its rigid, curved walls stand where the best of tents would blow away.

IN THE FOREST STEPPE, WARM WEATHER BRINGS MONGOL WOMEN OUTSIDE THEIR YURT TO COOK AND SEW. MEN KEEP THEIR HORSES CLOSE BY

THE LIGHT, COLLAPSIBLE FRAMEWORK of a yurt, with its latticework of wooden laths tied together with leather thongs, is so practical that even city dwellers often prefer it to a house.

THE ENTIRE BELONGINGS of a nomad family, yurt and all, are packed on their camel as they leave for summer pasture. A noose at the end of the man's 18-foot-pole serves as a lariat.

A MONGOLIAN YURT VILLAGE, WITH FENCED YARDS AND SHEDS FOR HAY AND LIVESTOCK, PROVIDES A SEMIPERMANENT WINTER REFUGE

PUSHTUN NOMADS leave the mountain slopes of central Afghanistan behind them as they begin a month-long migration south some 250 miles to warmer winter pastures. Each spring and fall in this part of the steppe, nearly two and a half million people make this trek. Day after day, while their livestock range the roadside, they plod along, leading camels piled

high with blankets, tents, poles, cooking pots, babies, chickens and whatever else the nomad family owns. Toward evening, the women and girls will fan out on either flank to scour the countryside for twigs and dried dung to burn in the night's campfire. The men, as they walk, play lilting melodies of native songs on a variety of indigenous string instruments.

SPINY HORROR

SAINFOIN·

After Rain, a Burst of Color

When spring comes to the arid steppe lands, with life-giving rain, the harsh landscape is transformed for a brief time into a place of brilliant colors and beauty. First, bright green mosses and the blue-green alga *Nostoc* appear, then flowers such as those pictured here carpet the countryside, and soon the grasses spring to life. The ephemeral annuals, such as bluegrass and white draba, will germinate, develop and ripen their seeds within a few weeks. Perennials like the crocus and grape hyacinth will store moisture in their bulbs to carry them through the dry summer. Every kind of plant in its own way prepares to weather the time until the next rain falls, be it only weeks or a full 12 months away.

BROOMRAPE

LIKE FLOWERING BOULDERS, a field of spiny astragalus shrubs provides protection from the wind for the small ephemerals on which sheep graze.

ROSE OF PERSIA

IRIS

PRZEWALSKI'S HORSE, NAMED FOR THE RUSSIAN WHO DISCOVERED IT ON THE STEPPE IN THE 1870s, IS THE LAST WILD HORSE LIVING TODAY

Survival in the Dry Regions

Despite their harshness, the arid regions abound in many varieties of animals. Most feed directly on the grasses and shrubs; others—snakes, lizards, some birds and mammals—feed on these plant eaters. Each animal has particular adaptations for survival in its environment. Thus the gazelle antelope not only can travel great distances in search of grass, but is also able to bound off at about 60 miles per hour to escape such predators as wolves. On the other hand, various small rodents protect themselves from climate and predator alike by digging burrows. Abandoned marmot holes become the daytime hideouts of the corsac foxes that feed at night on rodents and insects. They are particularly adapted for life on the flat plains, with their large, keen eyes, their long slender legs, sharp hearing and acute sense of smell.

GREAT BUSTARDS weigh as much as 30 pounds, prefer walking to flying. Like other large steppe animals, they are extremely wary and keep predators at a distance.

THE SAIGA, the strangest of all antelopes, lives on the open plains of the steppe, weathering the subzero winters and blistering summers. Its bulging nose is as useful as it is bizarre: the nostrils open downward as protection against windblown snow and sand. It was once hunted almost to extinction for its horns—sold in China for $250 a pair and used as medicine.

THE SWIFT AND WARY KULAN, the wild ass of Mongolia, is specifically adapted for survival on the flat and treeless plains. As much esteemed for its meat as for its hide, it has today been hunted close to the point of extinction—not an easy task considering the remote country into which it has retreated. Nearly as fast as a race horse, the kulan almost from

birth can escape its chief predator, the wolf, and before the use of firearms, could be taken by man only in cleverly laid ambushes. No kulan was ever known to have been broken to the saddle, though a few were tamed. Like the other ungulates of the arid regions, the kulan can live on incredibly scant fare: brackish water and dried grass are all it gets some seasons.

VIRGIN FOREST, one of Europe's last, lies in the heart of the Polish preserve of Bialowieza (*left*), where some 11,000 acres of oak, hornbeam, ash, elders, giant conifers and peat bogs shelter rare wildlife, including bison and lynx. Today farms and cultivated forest usurp much of the deciduous belt (*above*).

5

A Forest Primeval

and Its

Survivors

ANYONE traveling in Europe today, across France and into Germany, say, would find it very difficult to imagine what this part of the continent must have looked like only a thousand years ago. The wheatfields of the Beauce and the plateaus of Champagne in France, the vineyards of the Rhineland, the potato fields of northern Germany and the Jutland pastures—all these, clearly, have been created by the hand of man. Yet all the evidence—local chronicles, the study of place names, the analysis of pollen preserved in peat deposits—leads to the same surprising conclusion. From prehistoric times right up to the Middle Ages the greater part of western and central Europe was one immense deciduous forest, broken only here and there by heaths or swamps.

It is true that as early as Neolithic times, some 10,000 years ago, the first farmers began to attack the forests of Europe with fire and ax. But as they were few in number and their axes were of stone, the destruction they wrought was not very great. From 1050 A.D. on, however, the work of European deforestation proceeded on a truly heroic scale. Farming began it; it continued with the growth of cities and industries. It is only in the last hundred years that uncontrolled deforestation has been halted in Europe, and the amount of wooded

EURASIA'S FORESTS TODAY

There are still some 5.5 million square miles of forest in Eurasia, one third of the continent's total area. But not every section has its share, since some parts have suffered more than others from deforestation, and poor soil or climate has always prevented the growth of trees in certain places. How the different parts of Eurasia fare today with respect to forests is diagrammed in the blocks below: each square represents 500,000 square miles of area, the part that is still forested is in color. Thus, the first block shows that northern Europe (450,000 square miles) is about one half forested.

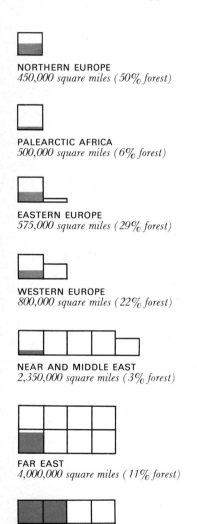

NORTHERN EUROPE
450,000 square miles (50% forest)

PALEARCTIC AFRICA
500,000 square miles (6% forest)

EASTERN EUROPE
575,000 square miles (29% forest)

WESTERN EUROPE
800,000 square miles (22% forest)

NEAR AND MIDDLE EAST
2,350,000 square miles (3% forest)

FAR EAST
4,000,000 square miles (11% forest)

U.S.S.R.
8,600,000 square miles (51% forest)

land has ceased to shrink and, in some countries, even begun to increase. At present, forests cover about 7 per cent of the territory of Great Britain, 21 per cent of France, a quarter of Poland and more than a third of Czechoslovakia. But the forests of today are by no means counterparts of the past wilderness. On the whole, the native trees of ancient times are scarcely represented. They have been replaced by trees from other latitudes, even from other continents. For example, the expanding demand for timber and pulpwood has led to increased plantings of quick-growing conifers. Even treeless barrens have been turned into evergreen forest. A century ago, Les Landes region in southwest France was a monotony of marshes and heaths marked only by occasional clumps of maritime pines and a few stunted oaks. Today this area, its marshes drained and its dunes stabilized, forms an unbroken pine forest of two million acres. Both in composition and distribution, therefore, today's wooded regions of Europe differ noticeably from the forest covering of a thousand years ago.

HISTORY does not tell us precisely the make-up of western and central Europe's forest in its primeval state. However, if we combine our knowledge of the environmental preferences of various plant species with a study of ancient pollens, we find that certain trees predominated in one place or another, depending on climate and the type of soil. The beech, for instance, flourished in unmixed stands wherever the rainfall was high and the soil well drained. This splendid tree, sometimes standing 130 feet high, provided lofty canopied forests, uninterrupted for miles. During the five to eight months of foliage each year, the beech forest floor was shaded; except for holly shrubs there was little underbrush. This damp, shady atmosphere was exactly right for the development of young beech saplings, which are extremely sensitive to direct sunlight and sudden changes of temperature.

The deciduous oaks of western Europe, on the contrary, were light-loving plants, and their saplings thrived in strong sunlight. Even in mature forests, where some oaks attained a height of 115 feet, the forest floor was sunlit and the temperature warmer than in the beech groves. There was, in consequence, an abundant, shrubby undergrowth of dogberry, birches, aspens and the like. On wet neutral-to-alkaline soils, in turn, the alder dominated to form gallery forests of varying widths along the bottoms of marshy valleys. On acid soils, on damp heaths and burned-out areas, stood a light birch forest similar to that found to the north on the edge of the tundra.

Despite its dominance of primeval Europe, the deciduous forest was and is absent from all the vast central portion of Palearctic Eurasia. There we find, instead, an abrupt change from a northern conifer forest to the land of prairie and steppe described in the previous chapter. Separating forest and steppe is a relatively narrow belt of thinly wooded oak or birch. Not until we travel half a world away, to northeastern Asia, is deciduous forest once more to be found. There, in the Amur and Ussuri river basins, we discover the Manchu forest, with oak, maple, ash and lime—trees very close to those of western Europe, although possessing characteristics of their own. In the undergrowth, a wild grape flourishes, as does the yellow angel-twigged magnolia vine with its lemon-scented bark. Finally, at the eastern limit of Eurasia, in Japan, stand fine climax forests of beech, maple, oak and birch.

Just as the primeval forest of Eurasia was somewhat different from the woodlands we know today, so was the animal life of the region. It is true that various present-day grazers and browsers—the red deer, the roe deer and the wild boar

—were dwellers in the Hercynian forest of Caesar's time, although we have little knowledge of the relative abundance of these animals or the habitats they preferred. But when Caesar described the fauna of *Hercynia silva*, it was to the most impressive of its herbivorous inhabitants—the aurochs, or European wild cattle—that he awarded the place of honor. He claimed them to be the size of small elephants, an exaggeration that makes it doubtful whether he ever actually saw one.

When reading the accounts of ancient authors, it is often difficult to be sure whether the aurochs or the European bison is being described. But there is no doubt that the aurochs had long haunted the forests of temperate Eurasia and even roamed outside the completely wooded regions. This mighty ungulate's remains have been found from Spain to England and southern Sweden, and from France to central Asia and the Near East. The art of thousands of years —from the Lascaux cave paintings in France to the Maikop silver vase and gold figurine from Russia and the Augsburg tableau in Germany—allows us to get an idea of the aurochs' appearance and color. In the 16th Century, the Swiss naturalist Konrad von Gesner, who collected much valuable information about these animals, described the male as resembling an ordinary black bull, but larger and with longer hair. It had rather slim horns that curved forward and curly hair on the forehead. Aurochs cows and calves were lighter in color.

Extremely agile and fierce, these gigantic cattle were not easily tamed. In summer they came out of their forest in herds and swept through the cleared fields. In autumn they gorged themselves with acorns and grew fat. In winter the herds were inclined to break up, and isolated individuals would crop the bare forest's buds and shoots. These habits doomed them. During the Merovingian period (500-751 A.D.), the aurochs were already so scarce in most of France that the privilege of hunting them was reserved for the king, but the great beasts were still plentiful in the wilder forests of the Vosges up to the 12th Century. They lasted a hundred years longer in Prussia, and in Lithuania until the early 15th Century. But by the 16th Century, the aurochs was to be found only in the western Polish province of Mazovia, where a herd of the giants dwelt in the royal forest preserve of Jaktarovka, 35 miles southwest of Warsaw. In 1599 this herd numbered no more than 24 and the last female died in 1627.

During the final centuries of its survival, the aurochs apparently interbred with domestic cattle. The wild cattle from the Camargue of France, as well as some domestic animals from Corsica and Spain, retain to this day the horn formation and the coat of the now-vanished Hercynian giant.

THE aurochs was not the only herbivore of Eurasian prehistory. In Pleistocene times, during interglacial periods, flourished the great bison—larger than any species of today and with varying horn structures. It later died out, but it is from this ancestor that the three subspecies we know today, the European and the American woods and plains bison, are descended. These survivors are capable of interbreeding and have similar habits, the differences between them being largely a result of their geographic isolation. The European bison is smaller than its American cousins, has a less massive head, shorter ears and a longer tail.

Although less studied in the wild than the American subspecies, the European bison appears to be essentially a forest animal, attracted to thick, shady woods that contain grassy or marshy clearings. In preference to grass, it feeds chiefly on the branches, shoots and bark of trees and shrubs, and even on heather, lichens, acorns and mushrooms. The animals never gather in big herds.

Cows and calves form small bands of 20 to 30 head. The mature bulls are solitary and join the bands only at rutting time in August. Unlike its relative of the American prairie, the European bison never seems to have undertaken large-scale migrations. Instead, its general behavior seems closer to that of the north Canadian woods bison, which occupies a similar habitat.

At the dawn of history, bison inhabited the greater part of temperate Europe as far as the Caucasus and the middle Volga. In Aristotle's day, a few still lived in Bulgaria. In western Europe, records of their existence are to be found around Saint Gallen in Switzerland in the 11th Century and in Brandenburg, Germany, in the 15th and 16th Centuries. In East Prussia and in Transylvania, they apparently survived into the 18th Century. The forest of Bialowieza, on the Russo-Polish frontier, was for long their major refuge; 737 bison were estimated to be living there in 1914. But the strife of World War I and the Russian Revolution proved fatal. In 1921 not one of the wild Bialowieza bison remained. Another colony in the Caucasus met with the same fate; the last survivor was killed by a poacher in 1919.

The European bison today, in fact, would be no more than a memory had not a few animals from the Bialowieza herd been captured at the start of the century and sent to different zoos. Reproduction in captivity brought the population of purebred specimens up to a total of 370 head in 1963. Earlier, in 1952, a few of these animals were let loose in the Bialowieza forest. This herd successfully returned to its wild way of life and is now prospering. Further reintroductions in appropriate places are now planned.

ALTHOUGH neither aurochs nor bison were able to adapt themselves to the progressive fragmentation of their forest abode, three other primeval ungulates of the deciduous forest have been much more opportunistic. The red deer, the roe deer and the wild boar have disappeared only from places in Eurasia where no shred of forest refuge remains or from regions where they have been exterminated by hunters. Granted a minimum of protection, these three species can thrive perfectly well in the cultivated forests of modern Europe, even when these are located near large population centers.

The red deer is an extraordinarily adaptable animal. It is to be found both on mountain and plain, on Scottish heaths and in the Engadine forest of Switzerland, in the "wooded steppe" of southern Russia, even in the remnant groves of the Mediterranean. Each of these populations, of course, differs in size and antler structure. The average weight of an adult in Scotland is some 200 pounds. In the Carpathians it is 400 pounds, in East Prussia more than 400 pounds, and in the Caucasus as much as 550 pounds. These surprising size differences are entirely environmental and are apparently attributable to the amount of food available. Moreover, an unplanned experiment has shown that size increase can be remarkably swift. Small Scottish deer, taken from a herd whose average adult weight was little over 180 pounds and in which 14-point antlers were rare, were introduced in 1870 into the Morven Hills of New Zealand's South Island. Within 20 years, the descendants of these Scottish immigrants showed an average weight of well over 400 pounds, and antlers with more than 20 points were being taken.

Although the red deer may often be seen in groups, the two sexes actually live apart. The basic social unit is formed by the female, her last-born fawn and the yearling. The males keep to themselves in groups of varying duration and membership, and they quite often even feed in different vegetation belts on the

CLUES TO ANCIENT FORESTS

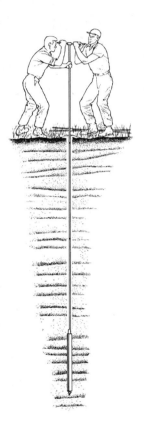

By analyzing pollen grains which have been preserved in peat bogs, scientists can determine what grew in ancient forests. Samples of pollen are obtained by driving a hollow collecting core into the peat (above). Going down, the core is rotated clockwise (below, left). This keeps an inner container closed and also prevents a small flange (jutting from the right side of container) from scooping up soil. When the desired depth is reached, the container is turned counterclockwise (below, right); this opens the inner core and the flange gathers in the sample.

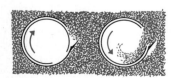

mountains. In autumn, the season of courtship, this isolation of the sexes is interrupted briefly. Then the males can be heard to "bell" in awesome concerts that break the evening calm. This belling, as the Swiss naturalist and painter Robert Hainard remarks, has a sound that is something between the lowing of a cow and a lion's roar. The ceremonies of courtship are not restricted to belling. At this period each mature stag takes over a display ground, often a small clearing, to which it comes late in the afternoon. Sometimes the clearing contains a wallow in which the stag rolls about voluptuously, interrupting these movements from time to time to butt the earth with its antlers. If a doe now approaches and shows interest, the stag follows her. But if another stag happens by, the pair of natural antagonists will bell in turn and the stag on its own ground will strike its antlers against a shrub. This behavior gives the impression of a ritual contest substituted for what would be a dangerous physical clash. It is seldom that actual battles take place.

S EVERAL other species of deer also are found on the wooded mountain slopes of Asia. The Manchurian wapiti is to be found throughout the temperate forests of Manchuria, and in Siberia from Transbaikalia to Ussuri and north into the Amur area. The sika deer, a small species with a speckled coat and rather modest horns, is still common in Japan and Manchuria. Sikas seem content with a sparse diet and thrive where ordinary red deer can barely subsist.

One famous Asiatic ungulate, Père David's deer, is now unknown in its original habitat, the great alluvial plain of northeast China. These extraordinary swamp animals bear unique antlers, the brow tine being unusually high and forked once or twice. As long ago as the Shang Dynasty (1766-1122 B.C.) the rare creatures apparently had ceased to exist in the wild state. They lived for more than 2,000 years in parks, however, and a herd of them still existed up to the 1920s in semicaptivity in the gardens of the Summer Palace outside Peking. It was there that they were discovered about 1865 by the famous missionary-naturalist whose name they still bear. The last of the Summer Palace herd died in 1921, but fortunately a few of them had been sent to England in 1900 at the time of the Boxer Rebellion. In Woburn Abbey, where they were installed by the Duke of Bedford, these few have given rise to a few semicaptive herds that are probably numerous enough to secure the future of the species.

The second of the still successful aboriginal inhabitants of Eurasia's deciduous forest, the roe deer, is small in size, has rather small antlers and an arched back—all characteristics that are admirably adapted to life in thick underbrush. Today, such an environment exists at the borders of forests or in fairly young tree plantations. And these are the places where the roe deer is generally to be found, even when the woods are not extensive. It is quite probable that the destruction of Europe's forests has actually favored the expansion of this species during the last few hundred years. Morning and evening, the roe deer may leave its forest haunts to visit neighboring fields, and in some regions it actually prefers the open heath. Its diet depends much less on grass than the red deer's, and in winter it will browse on pine needles, ivy and mistletoe. In spite of its enormous distribution—from the Atlantic to the sea of Japan, and from central Sweden and the Baikal region as far south as Greece and Szechwan—the species hardly varies at all and keeps to similar habits everywhere.

Despite their continent-wide distribution, individual animals of this species have a very restricted home range. Out of 1,000 roe deer marked in Denmark, two thirds remained all their lives within a radius of 1,000 yards of their birth-

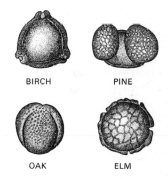

BIRCH   PINE

OAK   ELM

Four kinds of pollen grains found by the method shown opposite are illustrated above. Using radiocarbon techniques to measure the pollen's age, scientists chart the changing character of a forest. For example, 11,000 years ago birch and pine predominated in Scandinavia. A thousand years later the forest was pine and oak. Seven thousand years ago coniferous trees were replaced by oak, elm and other deciduous trees. A sharp decline in elm pollen at the 6,000-year level reflects human activity in cutting and burning.

place. They never form into large herds and, like other deer, the two sexes generally live apart. Summer is the season of courtship, and in preparation for this, the mature stags select temporary territories in late spring, which they mark with powerfully scented glandular secretions and which they defend against other mature males. If a doe presents herself, the stag will follow her for hours, muzzle outstretched and uttering a panting "hah-hah, hah-hah."

Development of the fertilized egg does not always take place immediately, so fawns are dropped during almost any month of the year. Twin births are quite frequent among roe deer, a fact that helps explain the rapidity with which populations have been observed to grow.

THE third of our modern Eurasian forest ungulates is the wild boar, which is found from the Atlantic to the Pacific. In the western half of its range, between North Africa and southern Scandinavia, the boar can live everywhere that the habitat is sufficiently "closed" for solitude. The northern limit seems determined more by the average depth of winter snow than by any other factor. Wherever this is over 28 inches, the boar will not be found.

Like all the other members of the pig family, the wild boar is basically omnivorous but with definite vegetarian preferences. Its diet is chiefly composed of acorns, beechnuts, chestnuts and mushrooms, as well as the roots, bulbs and tubers that it digs up by means of its tusks and its hard-tipped snout. This anatomical feature is useful not only for poking among dead leaves and forest humus, but also for rooting in meadows and in cultivated fields where the wild boar can cause considerable damage. Its vegetarian menu is varied at times by worms, insect larvae, eggs, snails, small rodents, young rabbits and sometimes even dead animals. The social unit is generally made up of several females accompanied by their young, and a herd may number as many as 35 individuals. The mature males sometimes move with the herd, sometimes lead solitary lives. The herds are nomadic and often travel great distances at night; studies have shown seasonal movements over a 300-mile area. Multiple births are the rule and litters can run to a dozen. When food is plentiful, there may be two litters in a year. Such fecundity does much to explain why the wild boar has persisted in western and central Europe in spite of being so widely hunted.

The two extinct and the three surviving large herbivores that we have now met were, of course, formerly the prey of both large and medium-sized Eurasian carnivores. Most of these carnivores have now disappeared from the greater part of their forest range. Of them all, the most important was certainly the wolf, identical in species to the wolf that survives to this day in North America. But the beast has been persecuted for a much longer time in the Old World than in the New, and it is scarcely surprising that Eurasian wolves are few and far between. That it has not been completely exterminated, the wolf owes to its cleverness and cunning, and its habit of roaming.

Wolves appear to have vanished first from the British Isles—around 1500 A.D. in England, 1743 in Scotland and between 1766 and 1770 in Ireland—but these animals were common throughout Europe until the beginning of the 19th Century. In France 2,131 wolves were killed in 1823; 60 years later, in 1883, the annual kill was still as high as 1,300. In 1910 about 50 were still taken in France by the special wardens called *lieutenants de louveteris*. In Switzerland, the wolves could survive only in thinly populated alpine valleys, and the last specimens were killed in the Graubünden in 1821 and in Tessino in 1872. Today, a few isolated wolf packs manage to hold out in the Iberian Peninsula, in Italy's

A DIFFERENCE IN SIZE DUE TO LOCATION

Although they are members of the same species, not all Eurasian brown bears are brown, nor, for that matter, do they all reach the same size and weight at maturity. The European brown bear (drawing) grows to a shoulder height of three and a half feet and weighs between 500 and 600 pounds; the Siberian brown bear (outline) stands half a foot taller and can weigh up to 800 pounds. The discrepancy in their sizes and weights may result from long isolation in forest pockets brought about by the destruction of woodlands, or from different diets and the effect of different climates. In very cold areas mammals tend to grow bigger.

Apennines and Abruzzi, and in Czechoslovakia, Poland and Scandinavia. But the only countries in which the animal is still in any way plentiful are Yugoslavia and the U.S.S.R. In the latter, a campaign for complete extermination, including parks and other natural reserves, is now being undertaken and the wolf may soon be little more than a memory there as elsewhere.

The brown bear, in spite of its greater size, has survived the persistent encroachment of civilization better than the wolf. This is probably due to the bear's relatively sedentary habits, which in their turn derive from an omnivorous diet and a capacity for spending the winter months in a state of prolonged torpor. Unless man drives it into regions where it is incapable of providing itself with food, the bear finds no need to poach upon cultivated ground and make a nuisance of itself to man, as the wolf has done. Thus it can survive surprisingly close to areas of dense population so long as the sanctuary allowed it corresponds to its natural tastes and is large enough for its needs.

The Eurasian brown bear belongs to the same species as the New World grizzly, and its habits are similar. Formerly it was to be found throughout Eurasia from the Atlantic to the Pacific. However, the progressive clearing away of the forest has broken up the brown bear's range into isolated pockets and this has had a definite influence on the variability of the animal's size and color. Although the brown bear has been gone from England since the 11th Century, from Germany since 1864 and from Switzerland since 1904, it is still present in appreciable numbers in some other European countries. There must be 100 or so in Spain, from 50 to 100 in the French Pyrenees, and probably another 100 in the Abruzzi and Trentino sections of Italy. In Yugoslavia, Albania and Bulgaria, greater numbers still find homes for themselves, while Scandinavia also has quite a few. But the U.S.S.R. is the country where brown bears are to be found in by far the greatest numbers. It is of some encouragement to conservationists to think that, while the wolf may never be protected by law, the bear is effectively safeguarded in many European countries, and the future of the species is thus provided for.

THE two wild felines of the primeval European forest were the lynx and the European wildcat. Both have become exceedingly rare; in fact, they have completely disappeared today from the greater part of Europe. One may wonder why these small or medium-sized wild animals did not succeed in adapting themselves to changing forest conditions, since the game they live on is still abundant there. Their counterparts in size—the fox and the badger—have managed to compromise with human activities and even to profit by them from time to time. The most plausible explanation is that these cats find it very hard to be near man; they have a systematic tendency to flee him even when the environment provides the food and shelter they need.

The lynx can now be found in sizable numbers only in the U.S.S.R., and even there it has become rare in the deciduous forest, favoring the evergreen taiga instead. In Sweden, a century ago, it used to be relatively common in the central and southern parts of the country. But persistent human pressure, which has become intensified with the increasing use of firearms, has driven the lynx into the less-populated northern districts. However, strict protection measures have been enforced in favor of the species since 1928, and it has now regained some lost ground. In Poland the lynx population appears to be larger now than it was before World War II. The species is protected in Yugoslavia. Elsewhere in Europe it is practically extinct, except in a few parts of the Carpathians and

A DIFFERENCE IN SIZE DUE TO DIET

Differences in diet have had marked effects on the sizes of Scottish red deer. Native representatives of this species stand about three and a half feet high at the shoulder and weigh around 200 pounds (drawing), whereas representatives introduced into New Zealand in 1870 (outline) are now approximately one half foot taller and 200 pounds heavier. Forced in Scotland to live off poor grazing land after forests were chopped down, they dwindled in size and numbers. But in New Zealand the milder climate and the richer food affected the red deer so vigorously that they regained in only 20 years their ancestors' lost stature.

in Spain, where a smaller race with an irregularly black-spotted coat holds out in sparsely populated southern and central areas of the country.

The European wildcat, formerly widely dispersed from the Atlantic to the Caucasus, still survives in Scotland, in Spain, in parts of France, in Belgium's Ardennes forest, in parts of Germany, in southern Italy, and in the mountains of the Carpathians, the Balkans and the Caucasus. On the Mediterranean islands of Corsica, Sardinia and Majorca, it is replaced by a related form; the African wildcat, the feline ancestor of the domestic cat. Indeed, the European species can be crossed with the domestic cat.

The European wildcat is much fiercer than the lynx, whose young can be tamed if taken away from the lair early enough. The English naturalist Frances Pitt, who tried this with wildcat kits, never managed more than a sort of armed neutrality despite all her efforts. Generally, the animals live alone or in pairs and they change their lair almost daily. Nocturnal in habit and excellent climbers, they stalk their prey and feed chiefly on rabbits, small rodents and birds.

ALTHOUGH we have examined only a few animals in this chapter, these few have served to illustrate the extent to which the forest fauna of Eurasia has been modified in the span of a few hundred years. Even though the wooded areas of many European countries are still quite large, certain animals—whether carnivore or herbivore—have shown themselves unable to adapt to the fragmentation of their sheltering forests, to the periodic clearing of timberland and to repeated human contacts. Decimated and driven off by hunters, they have either completely disappeared or have taken refuge in marginal areas where they do not necessarily find their natural habitat. Other animals, on the contrary, have profited by the new state of affairs and have moved into new niches, sometimes in unexpected ways. But it should not be thought that this two-way phenomenon is restricted to the larger mammals. Many changes have occurred in the distribution of small mammals, of birds, of fresh-water fishes and even of insects. Some of these changes have come about because of deliberate or involuntary introductions of new species. Far more are the result of man's own radical changes of the countryside.

Not only do some species become scarce while others prosper under these circumstances, but the areas of distribution of many animals also change without visible explanation. The serin, a small finch, was a sedentary Mediterranean bird only a hundred years ago. But from the 19th Century on, the species began to expand its range northward beyond the Alps. In this way the serin eventually reached central Europe, where it nested here and there in farmlands. By 1922, it had reached Holland, and in 1931, north Germany. By 1938 it was in Lithuania, by 1942 in southern Sweden. The bird came to Denmark in 1948 and to the channel coast of France in 1956. At the same time, these new northerners changed from sedentary to migratory habits and flew south each year to winter in the Mediterranean area!

What is a clear-cut case of human influence in respect to the bison—which would now be extinct but for zoo breeding—is less immediately evident in the case of a Mediterranean bird. Would the serin still be a sedentary southerner were it not for man's thousand-year labor of turning the European wilderness into farmland, orchard and pasture? The answer awaits further studies of similar events. But this much appears certain: better than anywhere else in Eurasia, the still undeciphered history of Europe's deciduous forests can teach us how human activities directly and indirectly influence animal life.

THE LITHE-BODIED WEASEL LIVES IN A HOLLOW FORMED BY ROOTS. SQUEEZING INTO SMALLER PLACES, IT RAIDS WOODLAND NESTS OF MICE

The Lost Wilderness

Although virgin wilderness still exists in Manchuria and Japan, the European forests are mostly second-growth woodlands, populated by deer and smaller animals. Only in Poland and in the Carpathians and the Caucasus are the tracts of deciduous forest old and dense enough to support bear and lynx. The fabled symbol of the wild, the wolf, has nearly disappeared from western Europe.

IN THE BIALOWIEZA FOREST, small bands of cows and calves stay together through the summer until the bulls join them in August (*above*). The mothers, perhaps because of an ancient fear of wolves, are so protective of the young that they will even drive off pheasants intruding on their range. To breed successfully, they need a rich diet of browse and pasturage,

ADULT BULLS, more rangy than the American bison, stand six feet at the shoulder and weigh about a ton. In medieval Germany, they were pitted against wolves in public arenas.

BELLOWING AND ROLLING in the dust are rituals of the rutting season. Full-scale battles between rivals rarely occur in the wild, since bulls usually run from stronger challengers.

The Return of Europe's Bison

Unlike its cousin, the American buffalo, which was literally shot off the Western plains, the European bison, or wisent, owes most of its troubles with man to the clearing of the primeval forests. For it is a denizen of the woodlands, and from about the Sixth Century, the population declined until, in 1921, no bison survived in the wild. But today, from a nucleus of 30 captive animals in Britain, Germany, Holland, Poland and Sweden, breeders have brought the herds back to 370 head, or about as many as enjoyed the protection of the czars of Russia in the Bialowieza at the end of the 18th Century.

usurped in recent times by herds of red deer. The wild bison were gone from this sanctuary for nearly 30 years. In 1952, it was restocked, and the present herd numbers about 40.

TO THE CHINESE, PERE DAVID'S DEER HAD REINDEER HOOFS, STAG ANTLERS, A CAMEL NECK AND A DONKEY'S TAIL

The Once and Future Herds

Partly because of an ability to thrive in second-growth woodland, the antlered tribes of Eurasia have fared far better than bison in the shrinking forests. The red and roe deer have maintained their distribution throughout Europe. The deer named after the French naturalist Père David, however, has been entirely a park animal for centuries. Knowledge of its former range on the low-lying plains and river flats of China comes solely from pieces of bone and antler found in buried cities and peat bogs of the Shang period, about 1766 B.C. Its broad hoofs are suited to walking in a swamp, probably its original habitat. Today the large herd at Woburn Abbey, England, still has a natural affinity for water and water plants.

THE RED DEER, similar to the American wapiti, made its way into northern Europe after the last ice age. In Germany and the area now covered by the Baltic Sea, an entire society of red-deer hunters wore their hides, ate their meat and fashioned spears from their bones. Now, 8,000 years later, herds of these hardy deer still prosper in Britain and in Europe.

SUMMER COATS OF THE ENGLISH FALLOW DEER are usually roan-colored with white spots, as shown above, but a thousand years of protection has encouraged much variation, from white and fawn to black. Stags weigh up to 200 pounds and carry huge palmated antlers shaped like those of the much larger Irish elk of the Pleistocene, now extinct. The present

JAPANESE SIKA, a small deer with a conspicuous white rump and four-point antlers, was first described by a Western scientist in 1838. A full-grown stag may weigh only 75 pounds.

The Sika and the Fallow Deer

The Chinese and Formosan sikas have suffered both from the decimation of the forests and persecution by man. Because their antlers are believed to have medicinal powers, they have been so persistently hunted that survival may depend on captive herds in other lands. The smaller Japanese sika, however, is not only numerous in its native forests, but also runs wild wherever it has been introduced—in New Zealand, Europe and America. The scream of the rutting sika stag now breaks the stillness of November nights in Maryland, where five deer released on James Island in Chesapeake Bay in 1916 have increased to more than 1,000, overflowing to other islands and the mainland.

Fallow deer, originally from the Mediterranean region, were long ago imported to northern Europe and England, where they are plentiful today in the parklands and open forests. In the countries of their origin, wild fallow deer are now found only rarely—for example, in the mountains of Spain.

population is descended from stock believed to have been introduced by the Romans. Well established by the 11th Century, the herds are now estimated to number about 9,000.

THE AZURE-WINGED MAGPIE has strangely isolated ranges, persisting in wooded regions of eastern Asia and Spain. The Japanese variety (*above*) has spread to farmland and suburbs.

Birds and the Shrinking Forest

Destruction of the virgin forests has had a mixed effect on Eurasia's bird population. Some of the species that depend on extensive stands of large, old trees, such as the eagle owl, could not adapt to new habitats, and are now extremely rare. On the other hand, game birds and numerous small songbirds have actually benefited from the clearing of the land. The second-growth forest and scrub provide all the food and cover they need. Orchards attract bullfinches, which feed on the buds of the fruit trees in such numbers that they often become pests. Notable among the back-yard birds is the robin. In

THE KINGFISHER, smaller than the American species, needs only a clear stream to fish and a bank in which to nest. Deforestation has not seriously cut its numbers.

THE GOLDEN PHEASANT, an Asiatic forest bird, presumably could adapt to cutover areas, since the ring-neck pheasant is now common in Europe and the U.S.

122

England this distant relative of the larger American robin has made a good adjustment to the disappearance of the woodland and now flourishes in hedgerows, parks and gardens. On the Continent, however, it is still a forest bird.

For those that can make the switch, the hedgerow is a fine environment. Its weeds, grasses and bushes offer a much greater variety of food and cover than the deciduous forest. The present density of birds in the forests of Europe varies from one to five pairs per acre, while in the hedgerows and copses there may be as many as 59 pairs per acre.

CONTINENTAL ROBIN, less tame than the British bird, usually stays in the thick undergrowth. European colonists named the American robin, with its similar red breast, after this species.

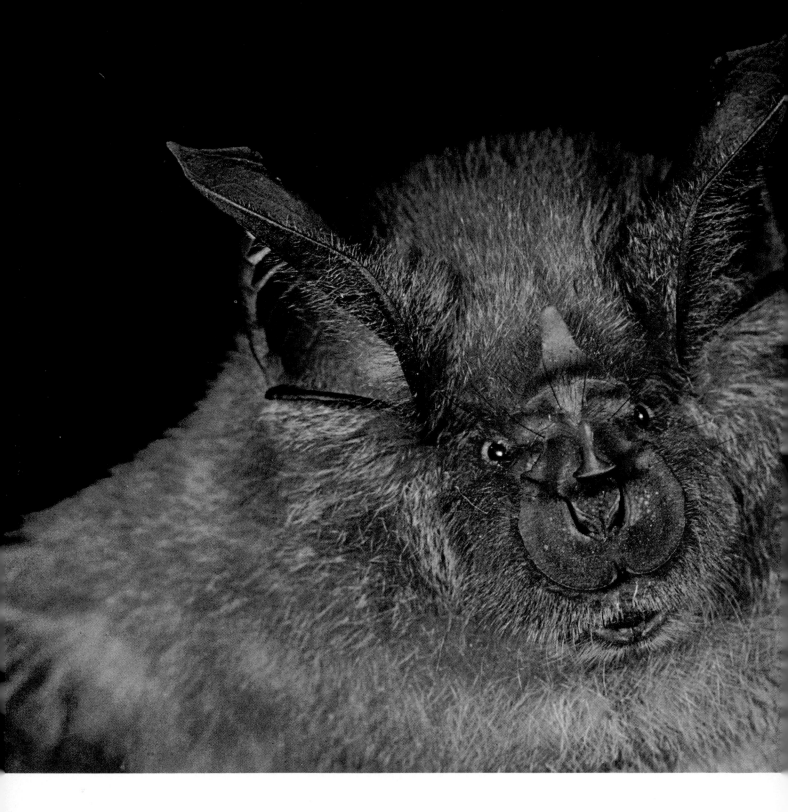

Opportunists at the Woodland's Edge

Throughout Eurasia, many predators live in forest cover but expand their feeding ranges to take advantage of the rich larder of insects, small mammals and birds in neighboring orchards, fields and barnyards. The most common of these opportunists are the various species of bats, drawn from dusky hideaways to throngs of insects attracted by bright lights. Others include the larger and bolder members of the weasel family—the badgers, martens and polecats —as well as five species of European rat snakes, which prey mostly on rodents, but also rob birds' nests, both in the woodlands and cultivated areas.

ROBBING A SHRIKE'S NEST is the Aesculapian snake (*above*), symbol of the Greek god of health. Of Mediterranean origin, this rat snake also persists in western Europe in the areas where it was imported for symbolic purposes to Roman baths.

THREE YOUNG POLECATS scrap over a frog (*below*) which one had managed to catch. The diet of the adults includes small rodents, but they also kill larger prey; the domesticated European breed, the ferret, is used for rabbit hunting.

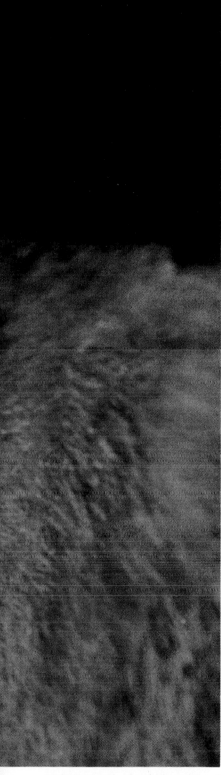

FIERCE FACE in the dark, enlarged five times, belongs to a horseshoe bat common throughout Eurasia. Folds around the nose and mouth funnel its cry in a narrow beam that bounces off insects like sonar.

THE VERSATILE RED FOX, WHICH SUBSISTS ON RODENTS IN FOREST AND FIELD, HAS A SECURE FUTURE EVEN IN FARM DISTRICTS OF ENGLAND

Classic Prey—and Predators

Some forest dwellers have survived over the centuries at least partly on the strength of their reputations as game animals. The wily fox, a master at hiding its trail, and the wild boar, tusked symbol of courage and ferocity, have always been fostered by sportsmen who hunted them. Although boars have been extinct in England since the 17th Century, they still thrive in central Europe. Another familiar animal, the brown bear, is protected most effectively by its sluggish and retiring nature. With eight or nine square miles to call its own, the bear is able to forage and raise a family. By contrast, the wildcat, the lynx and especially the wolf are carnivores whose cunning only serves them if they can range freely over many miles. Today they have disappeared from all but a few remote wilderness tracts.

CUBS AND MOTHER brown bear stay together on their home territory for two years. Once common throughout Eurasia, bears are now most numerous in the Balkans and in Russia.

LARGEST OF WILD PIGS, the Eurasian boar weighs some 400 pounds. So dangerous was boar hunting, with spear and dogs, that a kill counted as a deed of chivalry in medieval Europe.

TREADING SILENTLY IN FALLEN LEAVES, A LYNX STALKS HARES. IN COLD MONTHS OF FOOD SCARCITY, ITS RANGE MAY BE 40 SQUARE MILES

HUNGER AND SEARCH for scarce prey bring the European gray wolf out of its remote wilderness haunts on rare occasions. This unusual photograph of one member of a hungry pair roaming the open countryside was taken in the Berry district of central France, where wolves were believed to be extinct. Persecuted from the times of the annual wolf hunts of

Alfred the Great to the vast extermination program now under way in Siberia, the survivors today avoid civilization. Belatedly, man has begun to realize this carnivore's many-faceted role in the forest. Deer, for example, unless pressed by predators to seek new pasture, stay in one place and exhaust the food. In Scotland, herd dogs now enforce these movements.

THE TAIGA, A SEA OF CONIFEROUS TREES 400 TO 800 MILES WIDE, JOINS WITH THE TUNDRA TO FORM A CONTINUOUS BAND ACROSS EURASIA (MAP

6 The Land of the North

BELOW). THE BOGS AND LAKES THAT DOT THE FOREST SEEN ABOVE WERE LEFT BY GLACIERS THAT COVERED THIS LAND ABOUT 25,000 YEARS AGO

I T is an old and honored rule of thumb in biology that the changes in life forms—both plant and animal—that are encountered as one moves nearer to the realm of polar cold can be matched with the changes one discovers on climbing higher and higher toward the permanent snow fields of the great mountains. In a region as vast as Palearctic Eurasia, both an enormous sub-polar wilderness and a plentiful supply of lofty ranges are to be found. As we shall see, the old rule of thumb has more exceptions than are comforting to contemplate, but the two great Eurasian zones of cold indeed share one characteristic in common. Both of them lay until recently almost outside the ken of civilization. Neolithic society and the later high civilizations of antiquity both developed far to the south in the over-all region of the Mediterranean, whereas the industrial revolution confined itself to the lowland areas of western Europe, destroying much of its remaining forests in the process.

The subpolar zone consists of that immense sweep bordered on the north by the Arctic Ocean and on the south by latitude 55° N. As recently as the 1800s it was the domain only of visiting trappers and a few indigenous nomads who remained completely on the fringe of the cultural currents of West and East. Among these nomads, the Lapps are perhaps the best known. The tribal names of a half dozen others—Samoyeds, Voguls, Ostyaks, Chukchi, Koryaks, Yukaghir—are familiar only to the ethnologist and to the reader of explorers' accounts. It is only in the last quarter of a century that any towns of importance have arisen in northern Siberia, and even now this civilized penetration is largely confined to the valleys of the region's three great rivers—the Ob, the Yenisey and the Lena. This paucity of population is due in the main to the northland's limited agricultural possibilities. Northern Eurasia thus remains today almost in its original state, scarcely touched by man's hand. It is the last great bastion of untamed nature remaining in an otherwise densely populated continent.

FACING the Arctic Ocean, the entire northern coast of Eurasia is characterized by tundra, a treeless, low vegetation of hardy plants and dwarf shrubs which must do all of its growing, blooming and seed bearing in two or three months. There plants must take their nourishment from a soil that thaws to a depth of only a few inches during the brief Arctic summer. Below this thin layer the earth remains perpetually frozen in a zone of permafrost extending from Cape Kanin, on the west, for about 5,000 miles to the Bering Strait. It underlies not only the whole of the tundra, but a large part of the next most southerly zone as well. Many measurements have been made to see how far down into the earth the permafrost extends. The record for Eurasia is held by Amderma, a tiny spot on the Kara Sea, where drillings 700 feet deep found the ground still frozen.

On the polar fringe of the tundra, the annual precipitation is a scant seven to 12 inches. As a result, there is never any great depth of snow and the plants are poorly insulated against winter cold. Farther to the south, however, the tundra enjoys greater snow and rainfall. Here, particularly along the river valleys, the typical dwarf growth gives way first to bushy willows and birch trees, then to firs and larches, although these are stunted and few and far between. Thus by southerly stages one reaches the wooded zone of the tundra, borderland of the distinctive northern forest that extends in a single enormous block from northern Scandinavia to the shores of the Pacific.

This is the taiga, until recently an almost virgin forest. It is made up mostly of conifers: Norway spruce and Scotch pine in Scandinavia and European Russia, grading off to Siberian fir and spruce, and Siberian and Dahurian larch in Asia. Mixed with these conifers are such deciduous trees as birch, aspen and alder—the birch in particular standing everywhere as the most northerly sign of the taiga. Farther to the south, in the heart of the coniferous forest itself, birches still abound, springing up in dense groves where the conifers have been cut or burned down. Here and there, the monotony of the forest is broken by marshlands blanketed with red bog moss. These are more common in the west than the east; as one penetrates beyond the Yenisey river, they become rarer and rarer due to lower rainfall, decreased humidity, high summer heat and better natural drainage.

The forest is also broken by the three aforementioned rivers and their tributary streams which run from south to north to drain into the Arctic Ocean. On both sides of each river occurs quite a different kind of landscape, the *luga*. This low-lying grassy prairie owes its existence to repeated, more or less regular flooding by river overflow. Its ecological importance is considerable because it is the only natural prairie in an otherwise continuous forest belt.

From the viewpoint of the biologist, the Palearctic region of the Old World and the Nearctic region of the New World are one—particularly in their tundra and forest areas. This is emphasized by the striking similarities shown by their plant and animal life.

In the Old World, for example, the reindeer fills the role played by the caribou in Alaska and Canada. Indeed, most authorities now seem to agree that caribou and reindeer are a single species. Both animals make long annual migrations to pass the winter in the wooded tundra or even in the forest. Wild reindeer are still quite common in the greater part of Eurasian tundras, but for nearly a century they have been extremely rare in Lapland in northern Scandinavia. The Lapps have systematically hunted them because they interfere with the herds of domesticated reindeer.

Unfortunately the reindeer of Scandinavia and the U.S.S.R., whether domesticated or wild, are menaced today by another sort of man-made danger —radioactive fallout. Certain by-products of atmospheric testing—notably strontium 90 and cesium 137—become concentrated in lichens, a favorite reindeer food. This, in turn, results in an even heavier concentration of radioactive isotopes in the reindeer themselves. Among Swedish reindeer this has already reached 250 times that of beef cattle living in the same region—far above the level deemed safe for humans. This is not without danger to man. Tests of reindeer-eating Lapps in Sweden have revealed cesium 137 concentrations 30 to 40 times higher than the average for inhabitants of southern Sweden.

Although it may winter in the forest, the reindeer is basically a tundra animal. The true forest ungulate of the Eurasian taiga is known in the Old World as the elk and in the New World as the moose. This impressive herbivore is found continent-wide, from Scandinavia and East Prussia in the west to eastern Siberia and Manchuria. As with reindeer and caribou, the North American moose is quite clearly no more than a geographically isolated race of the Eurasian elk species. The habits of both are remarkably alike: their attraction to humid forests, their taste for willows and aquatic plants, their inclination toward a solitary life, even their reproductive cycle.

AT the beginning of the 19th Century, the European elk had become so rare in Scandinavia that its extinction was feared. However, measures were taken for the animal's protection and, in addition, it seems that the elk reacted favorably to man's clearing of the forests, because the very shrubs on which the elk feeds sprang up in abundance in the cutover areas. There were only a few surviving elk colonies in the central provinces of Sweden between 1810 and 1850, yet in 1959 hunters were able to take 32,286 of these magnificent beasts without seriously reducing Sweden's elk population. Today, in winter, the wild elk may be seen literally at the gates of Stockholm. Moreover, this increase has been accompanied by a movement northward into the tundra of Lapland, where the species was previously unknown. In European Russia, too, the elk population has increased in a prodigious manner after a period of decline in the 19th Century. Elk can be found in great numbers throughout the Russian taiga, and even in the outskirts of such large cities as Moscow.

As is the case with the herbivores, the large carnivores of Eurasia's tundra and taiga—the wolf, the arctic fox, the wolverine and the brown bear—have their close relatives in North America. The smaller carnivores of the Palearctic, however, show a more limited distribution. The pine marten is essentially European and is not found east of the Ob river. In Siberia, its place is taken by the sable, known for its valuable fur, and in North America by the American marten. Among the rodents the similarity between Eurasian and North American species is, once again, very close. The Russian flying squirrel dwells throughout the Eurasian taiga, living in a manner almost indistinguishable from that of its American cousins. The widespread Siberian chipmunk has close relatives in Canada and the United States.

T HE abundant lemmings of Eurasia are equally close kin to those of North America. Any mention of these small rodents brings to mind the so-called "mass suicides" to which the Norway lemmings are supposed to be addicted in years of overpopulation. Recent work by Finnish, German, Russian and Swedish ecologists has shown that the reality is not equal to the legend. To begin with, the lemmings migrate twice each year and not only in years of overpopulation. They winter in Scandinavia's mountains, living under the snow and feeding on mosses, grasses and other fodder that stays partly green under the protective snow blanket. The first litters of the year are born in this snug haven and, with spring, the lemmings move down the mountains to their summer range in a journey that may take them only a thousand feet lower in this alpine zone or may lead them on into the forest belt below. There they settle down to feed and produce additional litters. In September, they migrate uphill again to winter quarters.

In ordinary years, the lemmings are not numerous enough for these movements to attract attention, particularly since they usually travel alone and at night. It is only when a combination of favorable conditions produces a "population explosion" that they are noticed moving in large numbers. The much-publicized mass drownings of lemmings appear to be the result of their accidentally crowding into natural traps, such as points of land between convergent streams. Lemmings, in point of fact, are quite good swimmers, although studies by the Finnish zoologist Olavi Kalela have shown that they enter the water with some hesitation and usually only if the opposite shore is in sight.

Nevertheless they do sometimes cross lakes or streams in considerable numbers. This, however, is anything but "suicidal." Observations made by the Swedish naturalist Kai Curry-Lindahl during a peak population season in 1960 suggest that when enough lemmings are crowded together in a small space, they will begin to behave in a way that, in human terms, might be described as mass panic. Tension among the animals, Curry-Lindahl believes, builds up as new arrivals pour in, and finally it becomes unbearable, triggering the animals into a mass movement. Off they go, not toward any particular destination, but moving in a steady direction. Then, if they encounter water, their natural reluctance to enter it is overcome by the tensions propelling them forward. If the stream is narrow, they simply cross it and keep moving. If it is wide, or if it is an arm of the sea, they will, naturally enough, drown.

Although the Eurasian tundra is alive with migrant birds from the south

A HAIRY PLANT

What appears to be the flower of one of the edelweisses, plants traditionally associated with the Alps but ranging to Siberia and even to South America, is, in fact, no flower at all. The real flower consists of tiny yellow clusters at the center of a star of fuzzy "petals," which are actually hairy white leaves. Such hairiness enables the plant to grow at chilly altitudes of from 5,500 to 7,000 feet, since the hairs trap and hold the sun's warmth. Despite this adaptation, edelweiss does equally well in low-lying gardens, especially rock gardens with well-drained alkaline soil and full sun, where its white leaves turn a pale green.

during the brief summer season, the coming of winter reveals that its permanent bird population consists chiefly of two land species. The willow ptarmigan is a vegetarian. An extremely hardy bird, it is able to burrow holes in the snow and can thus not only find nourishment, but can also protect itself from the cold in all but the worst of years. Even so, it is sometimes forced southward in a particularly bad season.

The other is a predator, the snowy owl. It feeds mainly on willow ptarmigan and lemmings, and its population fluctuates widely according to the abundance of its prey. In lean years, the owl also moves southward and is often seen far from its normal haunts. But when the summer sun shines 24 hours of the day, these two bird species alone cannot begin to make full use of the tundra's brief abundance of plant and animal foods. It is this seasonal surplus that attracts migrants—mainly waterfowl and waders—from temperate and tropical regions.

The variety of birds that inhabits the taiga the year round is, as can be imagined, far greater than in the tundra. Vegetation feeders are abundant and include such species as the magnificent capercaillie, whose distribution corresponds closely with that of the Scotch pine. The black grouse, although it prefers swampy heathlands and bogs, is found wherever there are good stands of birches. Another year-round resident is the hazel hen. Among the smaller eaters of the forest's abundant supply of seeds are the redpoll, the pine grosbeak and three kinds of crossbills. The forest's wood-boring insects support such species as the three-toed woodpecker.

With a relatively large bird and rodent population in residence throughout the year in the taiga, the daily food supply is assured for a variety of resident birds of prey. Most notable of these are four species of owls—the Lapland, Tengmalm's, hawk and pygmy owls. But, just as in the tundra, these native birds cannot begin to consume the taiga's summer bounty. Immigrants pour in, 270 species to the European parts of the northern coniferous forest alone.

THANKS to the work of a corps of devoted Scandinavian ornithologists, we know that the bird life of the taiga has undergone distinct changes in the past two centuries. Records for 64 species during this period show an increase in either population density or range for 34 species and a decrease in the case of 30. A detailed study has been made of the causes of these variations; surprisingly the activities of man have been directly or indirectly responsible for changes—either up or down—in only 16 cases. In 34, ecological factors quite independent of human activity are at the root of the matter. Among these natural events, the steadily increasing mildness of the Scandinavian winter since the beginning of the 20th Century seems to have played the most important part, making it possible for certain species to extend their ranges northward. Studies by Olavi Kalela of birds in southwest Finland confirm this trend. Of 25 species for which this area once represented the northernmost limit of their distribution, 11 have increased both in numbers and in breeding range during the past 50 years, while only six have declined.

This same tendency has also appeared in marine life: fish such as the John Dory, the red mullet and the bluefin tuna, formerly found only in more southerly waters, are now encountered off the Scandinavian coast.

If there is a precise distribution of cold-tolerant plants and animals in the tundra and taiga, it is reasonable to assume that the mountains will contain similar or identical forms, again distributed according to the amount of cold encountered. Examination of Eurasia's mountainsides reveals a whole series of

A TUSKED DEER

A strange inhabitant of the forested hills of eastern Asia is the musk deer. Not much bigger than a large hare and covered by a thick coarse coat, it differs from most deer in several other startling ways. The male does not have antlers, but does grow a pair of curved tusks, which thrust two or three inches from under its upper lip and are reportedly used for fighting during the rut. In addition, the male possesses a musk gland, located in the abdomen, whose odorous secretion has long been recognized as one of the best natural fixatives for perfumes —and has made the musk deer one of Asia's most ruthlessly hunted animals.

vegetation zones, the uppermost of which are indeed reminiscent of the sub-polar taiga and tundra. In Europe's central Alps, at altitudes between 6,500 and 8,000 feet lies an evergreen forest in which the Norway spruce, typical of the Scandinavian taiga, predominates. Still higher, between 8,500 and 10,500 feet, are found tundra plants such as the arctic willow.

The distinction between Eurasia's two zones of cold is borne out when we study their contrasting fauna. True, the mountain birds of Europe include some species that we have already met in surveying the tundra and taiga. The ptarmigan of the Alps and the Pyrenees is a near relation of the tundra's willow ptarmigan. The capercaillie of the taiga is also found in the Pyrenees, the Alps, the Carpathians and the Balkans. The pygmy owl nests in the Alps, the Jura, and the Carpathians. But other mountain birds, although they may be widely distributed from east to west, are completely unknown in northern latitudes. The alpine accentor is common to barren mountain regions from Morocco's Atlas range to the Japanese "Alps." The wall creeper, which flits like a but-terfly, its red wings in pleasant contrast to the gray of its body, nests from the Pyrenees to northeastern China. The snow finch and the yellow-beaked al-pine chough are in every major mountain range from the High Atlas to the Himalayas. None of these are to be found in the subpolar zone of cold.

The same can be said for the mammals. Of the typical mountain species, only the mountain hare is common to Scandinavia, the northern U.S.S.R., Ice-land, Ireland, Scotland and the Alps. Other classic mountain mammals—the alpine shrew, the marmot, the chamois and the ibex—are unknown in the tundra and the taiga.

The ibex, a spectacularly horned wild goat, is perhaps the most notable of all the mountain mammals. In prehistoric times, when the Pleistocene glaciers reached their maximum extent, the species was at home in low altitudes in the southern half of France, in southern Germany, in western Italy and in Bo-hemia, Moravia and Transylvania. It was heavily hunted by late Paleolithic man, who also depicted it often in his cave paintings. When the glaciers re-treated, the great goats took refuge in the Alps. By 1700 A.D., they had be-come rarities. They were gone from the Tyrol by 1706, from Switzerland by 1820 and from France by about 1870. Indeed the species might have become extinct had not Victor Emmanuel II, Italy's "hunter king," jealously protected the last wild survivors in his hunting reserves in the Piedmont (which now con-stitute Italy's Gran Paradiso National Park). There, the remnant troops of ibex have succeeded in re-establishing themselves, and the 1961 census counted near-ly 3,500 head. In the meantime, the animal has been reintroduced into Switzer-land (35 colonies and 2,410 head in 1960), France, Austria and Yugoslavia. The once-vanishing ibex is now well out of danger.

But what caused this alpine animal's pathetic decline between the time of the Renaissance and the late 19th Century? Another alpine resident, the chamois, has been just as heavily hunted and yet has managed to maintain it-self fairly well everywhere in the mountains. It has been suggested that the "lit-tle ice age" (1430-1850 A.D.) reduced the mountain area suitable for the ibex, which tends to avoid glaciers and deep snow fields, whereas the chamois is quite at home in them. Blame has also been thrown on domesticated goats. Formerly they were more numerous and spent more time in the high mountains than is the case today, and this could have cut into the ibex's food supply. The chamois, on the other hand, can feed equally well in the lower forests.

Both of these factors undoubtedly played a part in the decrease in the ibex population. But it is more likely that the main cause was the widespread introduction of firearms among mountain hunters. The ibex is far less shy than the chamois and can be approached to within a hundred feet or so, which is point-blank range. Finally, the ibex female is much less prolific than the chamois.

The ibex is an excellent climber, able to move about with disconcerting ease on steep, slippery rock slabs. To do this it relies on what, for all practical purposes, is a rubber shoe. Marcel A. J. Couturier, the French surgeon-naturalist, tells us that the underpart of the hoof is soft and supple, allowing perfect adherence to a supporting surface and a firm grip on the tiniest projection. Well adapted to jumping and climbing among the high rocks, the great goats will not enter the forest even in winter. Thus they are confined to altitudes varying from 5,000 to 9,000 feet, which inevitably exposes them to more severe conditions of hunger and cold than are encountered by the chamois.

Ibexes travel the high mountain meadows in flocks, the females with their young composing one social group, and the males, sometimes in bands a hundred strong, another. The male bands have a tendency to break up before the breeding season, which is the middle of winter. The ibex diet is largely grasses and herbaceous plants, supplemented by leaves and lichens.

As with other typical mountain animals, the ibex of the Alps has relatives widely dispersed throughout the high places in Eurasia. In Spain, small numbers of the Spanish ibex still survive. The Caucasus shelter the locally named tur, while the Altai, Tian-Shan and Turkestan ranges provide a home for the Siberian ibex. These geographical races show differences in the shape of their horns and in other morphological details, but actually the ibex horn structure can vary even within a single local population. Emphasis on these variations could lead to a taxonomist's nightmare and an impossible multiplication of supposed species. Bearing in mind that there are fertile hybrids between all these ibex varieties, it seems wiser simply to place them into a single superspecies.

THE chamois, like the ibex and the marmot, seems to have been an animal of the plain during the peak Pleistocene glaciation. Smaller and more daintily built than the stocky ibex, its remains have been found in northern Spain, in France, in south and central Germany, in Czechoslovakia, Hungary and Transylvania, and in northern Italy. Even nowadays, this "symbol of the Alps," as it has been called, is not exclusively an inhabitant of high places. Chamois are settled at an altitude of 2,500 feet not far from Bern and it seems most likely that, if it were not for the disturbing presence of humans, they would inhabit all the lower mountains. They are more wary than the ibex and are said to scent a hunter from a quarter to half a mile away.

The diet of the chamois is more varied than that of the ibex: it will browse young shoots and even eat mushrooms. Social groups are composed of females and young on the one hand and males on the other, but groups tend to be much smaller and the males are sometimes solitary. As with the ibex, the breeding season comes in the winter. Today chamois are found in the mountains of northern Spain and the Pyrenees in the west, thence eastward through the Carpathians, and in certain of the Balkan and Transylvania mountains as far as the Caucasus. They are unknown to the east of Turkey's Pontic and Taurus ranges.

Our survey of Eurasia's zones of cold must include two notable bodies of water and the distinctive life that these support. The better known of these is a sea that should more properly be called a lake, and the second is the deepest—

UPLIFT IN SCANDINAVIA

Marked changes in the salinity of the Baltic Sea and in the character of the surrounding land have taken place during the 16,000-year period since the glaciers that covered Scandinavia during the last ice age began to melt. Relieved of this enormous weight of ice, the land has been rising. Today the fastest uplift—four inches a decade (largest arrow)—is in the upper end of the Gulf of Bothnia between northeastern Sweden and Finland, and is shown on the map by the darkest shade of color. In surrounding areas (lighter shades), the uplift (shorter arrows) is slower, being only 0.8 inch per decade in southern Sweden.

and possibly the coldest—lake in the world. The sea is the Baltic, which covers 163,050 square miles near the western extremity of Eurasia's tremendous evergreen forest. It is often likened by geographers and historians to the Mediterranean because, like the latter, its only connection with the world's major oceans is through a narrow, shallow strait.

But this is their only likeness: in other respects, the two are as different as can be. The Mediterranean is deep, with trenches that reach 12,000 feet below the surface; the Baltic is shallow, with a maximum depth of less than 1,400 feet. The temperature of the Mediterranean is fairly constant and high, never below 55° F., whereas the temperature of the Baltic fluctuates with the seasons, and in winter a large part of its eastern end is covered with thick pack ice. But the biggest difference between these two closed basins of western Eurasia lies in their salinity. Because the rate of evaporation in the Mediterranean exceeds the intake of fresh water, it is extremely salty. The exact opposite occurs in the Baltic. There the sun is usually low on the horizon, the sky so often overcast and the temperature so cool that evaporation cannot catch up with the enormous influx of fresh water contributed by the 250 rivers that drain into it. Thus the saltiest parts of the Baltic do not contain more than eight parts of salt per thousand (39 parts in the Mediterranean) and, at the top of the Gulf of Bothnia and the Gulf of Finland the water is almost fresh. The Baltic is in fact the largest stretch of brackish water anywhere in the world. Such a characteristic implies a very special flora and fauna. Ocean-dwelling animals, while still abundant right up to the front door of the Baltic, decrease steadily the farther into the sea one penetrates. In the Kattegat, at the mouth of the Baltic, there are 75 species of marine fish, 92 species of clams, oysters and mussels, and 64 species of shrimps and crabs. These numbers have dwindled to 22, four and two respectively in the Gulf of Finland. On the other hand, fresh-water animals rise in abundance as one moves in. In the sheltered, shallow waters of the gulfs of Finland and Bothnia there are not only numerous fresh-water snails, but also the larvae of flies, dragonflies, May flies, caddis flies and even water beetles—all insects that are normally lake and stream dwellers. Fresh-water fish species here outnumber the marine ones: there are, among others, the familiar pike, perch, bream and various whitefish. Finally, the ringed seal of Arctic waters, which has colonized Ladoga and other Finnish fresh-water lakes, is a Baltic resident.

Toward the other end of the taiga belt lies Lake Baikal, with its record-setting depth of more than a mile. This is a truly frigid lake. Even its surface water is very cold, not exceeding 66° F. during the hottest time of the year. The ice on its surface is still four feet thick in May. Deeper down, the water temperature is almost constant, remaining close to 37° F. throughout the year.

This perpetual chill is extraordinary enough, but what gives Lake Baikal its greatest distinction is its animal life, many varieties of which are unique. In it are found the famous nerpa, or Baikal seal, close kin to the ringed seal; the viviparous Baikal cod and the egg-laying cottocomephorids, known nowhere else in the world; also unique snail families and one indigenous family of fresh-water sponges. Baikal is particularly abundant in small crustaceans, more than 200 different species of the shrimplike gammaridae family alone being known. Far removed indeed in distance and climate from the familiar European seas, this immense and frigid lake of the north points up once again the extremes that give Eurasia its extraordinary and variegated character.

COVETED FOR ITS FUR, HATED FOR ITS GREED, THE WOLVERINE WAS SO HUNTED THAT IT HAS BEEN DRIVEN TO REMOTE PARTS OF THE TAIGA

The Zones of Cold

South of the Arctic Sea lie two bands of vegetation—the tundra, or Arctic grasslands, and the coniferous forest, or taiga. Together they cover a fourth of the land of the Northern Hemisphere and almost half of Eurasia. Interrupted only by the Bering Strait and the Atlantic Ocean, they stretch in a continuous strip right around the world and have much the same plants and animals throughout.

A VERSATILE PREDATOR, THE WOLVERINE MAY FEED ON FISH AND FROGS AS WELL AS ON VOLES, HARES, DEER, OR BAIT STOLEN FROM TRAPS

Animals of the Tundra and the Taiga

In moving northward from the deciduous forest to the harsher conditions of the taiga and the tundra, a gradual decrease in the variety of animal life is noticeable. This is because a large number of warm-blooded animals are not able to adapt to extreme cold or to a long season in which the ground is covered with snow. Those that can, cope with the long winters in various ways. Many of the smaller animals, such as the field vole, tunnel underground and turn to their advantage the insulating blanket of snow which accounts for differences of as much as 70°F. between the temperatures of the bitter winter air and the ground below. Others, like ptarmigan and certain hares, get around on top of the snow by means of "snowshoes," or feathers on their feet. Still larger animals, like the moose, have long and stiltlike legs for deep snow. Fluffy coats which trap warm body air, pale coloration and thick layers of winter fat are other adaptations which are useful to animals that live in the tundra and taiga.

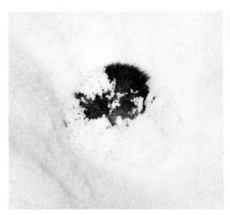
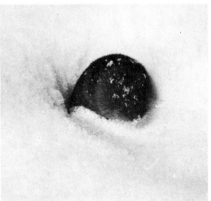
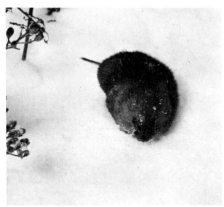

FAT AND CLUMSY, a field vole pokes its head out from a snowy tunnel to look for seeds. It is a favorite morsel for owls, its short life balanced by a reproductive rate that under ideal conditions could increase its numbers tenfold in six months.

PALE AND FLUFFY, the coat of the arctic fox serves as camouflage in the tundra snows and cuts down loss of body heat.

DARK IN THE SNOW, an otter frolics between meals. A waterproof coat and a sinuous body adapt it for life in the water.

SILKY WHITE in its winter coat, the varying hare turns brown in summer. Experiments have shown that molting is set off by changing day length. Animals kept on 18-hour days stayed brown all year, while those on nine-hour days turned white.

DISPLAY FIGHTING between two taiga-dwelling black grouse starts with a lunge (*top photo*) by one and continues (*bottom*) as both try to dominate each other by flapping their wings.

Grouse in the Taiga

Although most of the world's birds pair off in couples during the mating season, a few species behave entirely differently. Among these, the males gather in the spring to compete with each other for the favors of large groups of females. These polygamous birds include various members of the grouse family, such as the black grouse and capercaillie, both of which live in the colder regions of the Eurasian forests. Their peculiar behavior may well help them surmount the long winters in their harsh environment, since the survival of only one male is required to fertilize a large number of females.

The "aim" of a strutting, displaying black grouse cock is to intimidate other cocks so that it can establish its mating rights and gain a preferred position on the mating ground before the gathering of hens. The "fighting" is largely ritualistic since it seldom results in actual physical contact between males.

A FULL SWEEP of its wing by the bird at the left fails to intimidate its flapping adversary. Despite their aggressiveness, both birds have taken good care not to injure each other.

AT THE PEAK OF ITS DISPLAY, a male capercaillie fans out its tail like a turkey and stretches its head high. Grouse absorbed in these contests can easily be taken by hunters.

The Moor and the Tundra

Although it resembles the tundra superficially, the moorland that is found in many parts of Eurasia, most notably in the British Isles, is basically quite different. The main difference is that the tundra occurs farther north than the moor. It is characterized by subsoil that is permanently frozen from a depth of about three feet to more than 700 feet. This gives the tundra its open barren appearance, since trees cannot grow there, their roots being unable to penetrate frozen ground. Most of the tundra's scant precipitation is in the form of snow, and its vegetation consists of lichens, mosses, grasses, a few low shrubs and highly specialized flower-

ing plants—all adapted to a cold dry environment.

The typical moor, although it, too, is wild and windswept, and covered with low-lying plants, owes its nature to the recent ice age. Glaciers scoured away all of the fertile soil and when they retreated they left behind them a jumble of boulders, gravel, sand and clay, which are favorable only to the growth of such plants as mosses and heather. Many moors, notably those in Scotland, lie in areas of heavy rainfall. They hold water like sponges and are actually upland bogs where it is too wet for men to cultivate or for trees to grow. Dead plants sink into the bogs and over the centuries turn to peat.

WINDBLOWN AND BARREN, the Norwegian tundra is so frigid that the process of decay needed for good soil cannot take place. This limits its plants to those which can survive poor soil and intense cold.

BRIGHT AND COLORFUL, heather luxuriates on an English moor. Unlike the moors farther to the north, this area was once a forest. After man cut down the trees and fired the land, the heather recolonized the leached soil.

SODDEN AND BLEAK, a bog near Glencoe, Scotland, is covered with a mosaic of russet sedges and sphagnum mosses. Together they blanket a layer of peat—the "soil" that borders the ditch running through this photograph.

145

A NORTHERN CUSHION PINK, growing in the tundra, has the same dense boulderlike shape as the mountain cushion pink in the picture below.

The Telltale Birches

The similarity in habitat between the high mountains and the far north is underscored by similarities in vegetation. The cushion plants are an excellent example of this, their rounded form and closely bunched stems reflecting a common adaptation to the cold and wind— whether of the tundra or of the heights. The distribution of a single plant will often tell the same story. Birches may be found growing in many parts of Eurasia, but they do best in cool or cold places. Thus the finest stands of birch are found along the northern edges of the taiga —and on the higher slopes of the Alps.

A MOUNTAIN CUSHION PINK is nearly indistinguishable from its arctic brother (*top*). The cushion pinks flourish in cold regions of Eurasia.

ON A COOL ALPINE SLOPE a clump of white birches thrives. This species needs plenty of sun, and in time, as the conifers seen in the background crowd in, the meadow will become too shady for young birches to grow.

147

A GROVE OF STURDY BIRCHES IN FINLAND STANDS IN AN EMERALD COVER OF FERNS, WOOD SORREL AND GOUTWEED

SWOOPING SILENTLY, a Tengmalm's owl drops on a forest rodent. Like most other owls this species is slow-witted even for a bird. It is so easily approached in its daytime hiding places that it can often be caught by hand. Thus it has been nicknamed the blind owl—erroneously, for there is no proof that its sight is any worse during the day than it is at night.

148

THE HUMBLE DONKEY is one of the most useful domesticated animals. Originally from Africa, it gained a foothold in the Near East and subsequently spread into Asia as the land was drying up. It can get by on a diet of thistles and straw.

7

The Taming
of the Wild

WERE it possible for a band of pre-Neolithic hunters and gatherers to return to today's Eurasia in some miraculous fashion and tour all of the Palearctic from Spain to Japan, they would find a transformed continent. This transformation is not so much a matter of absences—lost animals and plants—as an astonishing abundance of new and unfamiliar species, brought about by the Neolithic revolution. "Neolithic" is a misleading term for this phenomenon. In the strict sense it refers only to a minor technological advance—the shift from flaking to polishing in man's techniques for making stone tools. Its real importance lies behind the name, for during this period man first began the domestication of animals and plants.

Considering the enormous importance of these twin accomplishments to the future of mankind, it is surprising that we know so little of the actual steps by which they came about. These are lost in the mists of prehistory, although a number of recent discoveries and surmises provide some fascinating clues to what probably happened. There is, of course, no mystery about the result. When man became able to develop reliable supplies of certain plant and animal species for food, clothing and even to work for him, he had within his grasp for the

UNUSUAL DOMESTICATIONS

In addition to important domestic species like the dog and cow, man has experimented off and on with other animals, like the five shown here. Strictly speaking neither falcon nor cheetah is truly domesticated, since they do not breed in captivity. However, their decline as tamed species results from a change in man's habits, not from any deficiency in the animals themselves. Bees and silkworms are domesticated only in the sense that they do what man wants them to do.

FALCON

Falcons were first used for hunting in Assyria and the practice was brought into medieval Europe by returning Crusaders. It quickly became a sport of the nobility and did not die out in Europe until nobility itself began to languish.

CHEETAH

The easily tamed cheetah is the world's fastest-running animal and has been used for coursing, like a greyhound, for several thousand years. Having little endurance, it is carried on horseback until the game is sighted, then sent after it.

first time the means of settling down permanently in one place. It was this that made possible the great cultures that followed, that permitted the enormous increase in human numbers, and that has worked such profound changes in the face of the Eurasian continent.

Today almost half of Eurasia is dappled with plants that were introduced during and after the Neolithic revolution. Luckily for man, this transformation has not meant a slump in the total annual production of living matter—both vegetable and animal—for Eurasia as a whole. Only in the Mediterranean zone has there been a reduction in productivity. Elsewhere it has held up well, despite the change in its character. And as far as animals are concerned, the total number of individuals of today's various domestic species far exceeds the total of wild herbivores that originally occupied these regions.

What has happened is that man has monopolized for his own exclusive benefit the greater part of Eurasia's biological productivity. In all low-lying areas with deep and rich soils, the former wild has become a sort of gigantic machine that produces the daily ration of calories required to feed human populations ever on the increase. Here the pre-Neolithic wilderness is now tolerated only in the form of cultivated forests, national parks, green belts and places for recreation, and all its wild animals are more or less regarded as competitors.

How, exactly, was the domestication of plants and animals accomplished? Let us admit that we will never be able to know the answer to this question with certainty, particularly in respect to why certain wild species were chosen for taming and others not. Nonetheless, study of the habits of today's primitive peoples, together with analysis of the behavior of the wild animals that are the ancestors of our domesticated types, proves extremely suggestive.

It is interesting, for example, that women and children of today's hunting and gathering tribes—such as the Guayaki of South America and various aborigines of Australia—take pleasure in taming and making pets of many small mammals and birds, even though these tamed animals are a drain on the resources of small groups always underfed and almost always on the move over wide expanses of hunting grounds. It is certainly possible that mankind has long possessed this sort of unmotivated affection for animals. Further, it seems probable that this sentiment is actually useful to peoples who depend on the chase for their livelihood—the idea being that through his making pets of wild animals, the hunter child will come to know their habits and reactions better, which, in turn, will improve his hunting skills as an adult and brighten his chances of survival in the battle for life.

Thus we can theorize that the hunters who were the distant ancestors of us all came to know at a very early date the habits of the mammals with which they lived in daily contact. One of the earliest things that they undoubtedly noticed was that certain species were naturally attracted to certain spots—a necessary first step in placing man near enough to animals to catch them alive. With herbivores, this meant man's taking advantage of their attraction to fresh grass springing up in burnt-over areas, to natural salt licks, even to places impregnated with human urine. In somewhat different fashion, early man was probably able to come slowly face to face with the jackals or wolves that hung around his campfires and to cement the relationship with an occasional bone thrown into the dark.

Then, as a matter of fact rather than theory, we now know that a young animal, however wild, will sometimes behave in a manner that must have astonished our hunter-ancestors: instead of fleeing with its parents or freezing against the ground, the young creature—at a critical age—will follow at the heels of any human who happens to pass by. This strange behavior is the result of a phenomenon that modern ethologists call "imprinting," a tendency among certain young animals, during the first few critical hours of life, to accept as their mother the first moving creature that they see. The substitute mother need bear little or no resemblance to the true mother—the animal behaviorist Konrad Lorenz succeeded in getting himself imprinted as the mother of a brood of freshly hatched goslings. The important thing is to be there at the right moment and with the real mother absent. The critical period is usually very short; in the case of ungulates it lasts for only a few hours just after birth. But the commitment, once made, is a strong one. I myself know of two cases in which a man crossing the East African savanna found himself suddenly "adopted" by a newborn buffalo abandoned by its mother. In both cases it required all sorts of stratagems to shake off the young animal.

DORMOUSE

Dormice were raised in great numbers by the Romans, who fattened them for the table in earthenware pots and attached much status value to their size. By the Middle Ages the practice of eating these small rodents had virtually died out.

It would have been an easy matter to bring such an imprinted animal back to a Paleolithic camp; the hard job would have been to keep it fed. The only way, then, would have been to find a wet nurse for it, and in the case of small mammals, a human could have filled this role. In New Guinea today, piglets often feed at human breasts and Ainu women are known to suckle bear cubs.

Many herbivores are already almost self-sufficient at birth. But animals born in a less developed state require a long period of mothering, which poses more delicate problems. Nonetheless, two modern examples—Lois Crisler's success with young wolves and Joy Adamson's with lion cubs—show how strong and lasting can become the ties between man and what are reputedly the most savage of animals. In fact, once tamed, it is often impossible to readapt them to the wild. Primitive man must have taken advantage of this phenomenon many times, and in the cases where the pets succeeded in reproducing themselves in captivity, the gradual process of selecting the most docile offspring for further breeding no doubt followed. This is a vital step in developing an actually domesticated strain—that is to say, an animal that will breed at close quarters to man and will remain under man's care.

HONEYBEE

Bees have served man since their first domestication in Egypt about 5,000 years ago. In Mesopotamia they were more useful as providers of wax for writing tablets than of honey. Beehives were used as weapons in battle as recently as 1650.

To theorize again, Paleolithic hunters must have learned to distinguish quickly which types of chance animal pets were the most adaptable and the easiest to handle. For example, most Eurasian ungulates do not make good herd animals, since the males and females live apart except at breeding time. There is one species, however, in which the males live more or less constantly with the females in promiscuous flocks. What is more, the males do not generally display any territorial behavior, and the females will adopt and suckle young that do not belong to them. This unique Eurasian ungulate is the wild sheep, or mouflon —the probable ancestor of one of the Neolithic's earliest domestic animals.

JUST as modern studies of wild Eurasian animals help us to get a better idea of how our hunter-ancestors may have been able to transform their erstwhile prey's fear into toleration and finally to dependence, each year reveals a little more about the times and places in which the domestication of animals may have occurred. The dog is probably the oldest of man's companions, and most likely derived from a subspecies of wolf that still survives in Palestine, Iraq and northern India. This is a small wolf; it seldom if ever howls and sometimes even barks like a dog. British prehistorian Frederick Zeuner held that it may have been domesticated in the Near East around 10,000 B.C. Russian archeologists

SILKWORM

Silkworm breeding began in China in 3000 B.C. and its secret was jealously guarded, since Chinese silk brought its weight in gold even in far-off Rome. The monopoly was broken in 536 A.D. by Syrian monks who smuggled eggs out.

working in the Crimea and Siberia have found what they believe to be the fossilized droppings of this same wolf species among fragments of human remains that date from an even earlier period.

Transitional stages between true wolf and true dog unfortunately do not exist as fossils—or if they do they have not yet been discovered. But dogs themselves go back a long way. At the famous English pre-Neolithic site, Star Carr in Yorkshire, a dog's skull that exhibits wolflike teeth has been found dating back to 7500 B.C. This is the oldest certain domestic dog thus far discovered, but in nearby Scandinavia, at levels that date around 6500 B.C. two *different* kinds of dogs have been found. One is small and the other large, but even the large one is smaller than the wild wolf of central and northern Europe. This discovery of two distinct and unwolflike races of dogs on the frontier, so to speak, of a still partly icebound northern Europe leads Zeuner to the conclusion that the species was originally domesticated well to the south and at a considerably earlier date. Further support for this viewpoint is the existence of an Egyptian pottery bowl, from the fourth millennium B.C., which shows four dogs—some of them indubitably of the race we know as greyhounds—led on leashes by a man. Though Yale mammalogist Charles Reed points out that the existence of such a specialized animal at this date indicates a long, although undocumented, period of selective dog breeding in the Near East, his conclusion is contrary to Zeuner's. "Dogs were first domesticated (so far as we can know now)," Reed states, "in northwestern Europe in the Mesolithic period."

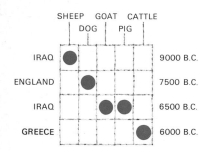

THE FIRST TO BE TAMED

When and where the five commonest domestic animals got their start with man is shown in this chart. It is noteworthy that for four of the five the association began in the Mediterranean region, that for three—sheep, goats and pigs—the probable beginning of the taming process was in what is today northern Iraq.

ONE of the crosses that the prehistorian must bear is that even an expert anatomist finds it difficult to distinguish between most of the bones of sheep and goats, particularly since what differences there are cannot be detected when the bones are broken up. The most useful remains for telling which of the two species one is dealing with are the cores of the horns. But even with this aid, archeologists face still another problem: how can one know whether the bones found during excavations are those of wild animals or of their domesticated descendants? As it happens, the internal surface of the horn core of the domesticated goat is flattened or lozenge-shaped, whereas that of the wild goat is rounder. One can be reasonably certain that such a morphological change did not happen in a day; thus, a flattened horn core may be considered evidence that its owner was a domesticated animal. This is all very well for goats, but the same rule does not work for sheep, and even among goats there is no way of telling whether a round horn core came from a truly wild animal or from one whose line might have been in the process of domestication for centuries.

Fortunately, today's archeologists have developed a sound, if indirect, criterion for estimating the extent to which these herbivores have passed from the wild to the domesticated stage. When a pile of remains contains bones of animals of all ages, as might be expected in a primitive hunter's bag, it is assumed the animals were wild. But when the proportion of young animals is much greater, as in the case where herds are culled for the cook pot, the assumption is that the animals were at least semidomesticated. Thus, at any given prehistoric site, when the proportion of immature animals increases abruptly from one level to the next, there is a near certainty that the change coincides with domestication. However, because this indirect evidence can be obtained only by a careful statistical analysis of a great many bones, we should not be surprised that the exact dates for the domestication of the sheep and the goat still remain uncertain. Only one fact is clear today: these tough, useful animals certainly preceded such other ungulates as the pig, the ox, the ass and the horse, in man's service.

The Zawi Chemi site lies in northern Iraq, near the famous Shanidar Cave. There, in the summer of 1960, American archeologist Rose Solecki brought to light a large number of sheep remains, 60 per cent of which were yearlings. The prehistoric inhabitants of Zawi Chemi apparently slaughtered the larger part of each season's lamb crop before they were a year old. The level at Zawi Chemi where this find was made gives it a date of about 8900 B.C.—substantially earlier than the first domestication of sheep was previously thought to have been. Five millennia later, in the 4000 to 3000 B.C. period, domestic sheep were spread from upper Egypt to Turkmenistan, in effect all over the then civilized world.

The first goats of certain domestication—using the diagnostic of flattened horn cores—turn up some two millennia after the sheep of Zawi Chemi, at Jericho in Palestine and Jarmo in northern Iraq. But it is fairly obvious that goats had been domesticated or semidomesticated in this region for centuries before this date (about 6700 B.C.). In general terms, then, these two ungulates may be said to have had almost an equal start as domestics in the Middle East, although there is some evidence that the sheep reached the oases of west-central Asia well ahead of the goat, whereas a sort of dwarf goat apparently moved up the Nile ahead of sheep. In short, sheep eventually got the upper hand in all Eurasia's temperate latitudes, while the hardier and less demanding goats were raised in the dry steppes and mountainous regions.

The domestication of the pig seems to have taken place a little later than that of the sheep and the goat. The excavations at Jarmo show that the remains of pigs are rare in the earlier levels, and all of these bones definitely belong to wild boars. Toward 6500 B.C., however, in upper levels of this village-farming community, there suddenly appear in large numbers the remains of pigs whose third molar teeth are shorter than those of the wild boars of the region. This reduction in tooth size, together with other skull changes, is a valuable clue in the story of domestication. For, just as in the case of the flattened horn core of goats, it enables archeologists to demonstrate an ancient association between pigs and man.

Unfortunately, so far as cattle are concerned, we have no such means at our disposal for saying with as much certainty when the domestication of these large ungulates began. The presence of cattle bones in a site at Banahilk in northern Iraq shows the existence of a cow that was distinctly smaller than the wild aurochs. This leads some authorities to believe that the animals were already domesticated in northern Iraq around 5000 B.C. Recent Near Eastern finds indicate a date at least 1,000 years earlier. In any case, the exquisite portraits of cattle, made in the fourth millennium B.C. and found on the cylinder seals of Warka and other early Sumerian towns, testify to the economic importance of these animals. In Egypt it appears that domestic cattle were not known until about 3200 B.C.

WE have not even this much detail for either the date or the location in which ass and horse were broken to man's will. For the horse, this event appears to have taken place in Eurasia's central steppe corridor, between the Ukraine and Turkistan, some time around 3000 to 2500 B.C. Unknown at Sumer, the horse was not introduced to the Near East until about 1800 B.C., nor to Egypt until about 1675 B.C., and was not found in Mycenae and the Greco-Cretan Mediterranean until about 1550 B.C. The first such animal to be hitched to chariots by the Sumerians, about 2500 B.C., was not the horse at all, but the ass of Asia, the onager. The unruly onager's career as a domestic animal was apparently short, for today's donkey is descended not from it, but from the African wild ass domesticated in the Nile valley about 3200 B.C. and long confined to northeastern Africa. It did not reach Palestine and Syria until much later.

The domestication of still another Near Eastern saddle, pack and draft animal, the one-humped camel, or dromedary, was even more recent; it appears to have taken place in Arabia about 1800 B.C. From there, this ideal desert beast of burden gradually spread into Mesopotamia and Palestine, but was unknown west of Egypt before the Roman era. As for the two-humped, or Bactrian, camel, the site of its domestication was probably central Asia, but where we do not know. All that is certain is that the Bactrian camel was found over much of Persia in the early half of the first millennium B.C.

Some zoologists would not yet claim the common cat as a truly domestic species, but rather as a sort of commensal, which may feed at man's table but is no servant. House cats first made their appearance in Egypt about 1600 B.C. and were used then, as now, to keep rodents in check. As stated earlier, they are descended from a North African subspecies of the Eurasian wildcat.

The various birds that have graced men's tables and provided a supply of eggs show both mixed origins and a varying antiquity. Both the goose and the rock dove, or common pigeon, are Eurasian in range. The graylag goose may well have been domesticated in Neolithic times and was certainly a domestic fowl in Egypt by the start of the New Kingdom (1580 B.C.). The rock dove was a temple bird used for sacrifices in the pre-Biblical Near East, a practice which was continued down through the time of Christ by the Hebrews. In contrast to these Eurasian native birds, today's most abundant barnyard fowl—the chicken—is an import, descended from the wild red jungle fowl first domesticated before 2000 B.C. in southeast Asia. This bird, for all its distant origin, reached the Near East as early as 1400 B.C., and by the Sixth Century B.C. had become the dominant domestic fowl in Mediterranean lands. Finally, today's largest table bird, the turkey, is a complete newcomer to Eurasia, having been domesticated by Indians in Mexico and imported to Europe by Spaniards in 1523 or 1524.

Goat, sheep, pig, camel, horse, donkey, cow, dog, cat and barnyard fowl: these are man's great achievements in domestication, the only ones, in fact, that have gained worldwide distribution. It is interesting that the first nine species are all descended from Eurasian wild ancestors, equally so that those ancestors still exist—except in the case of the cow, whose aurochs progenitor is extinct. What must not be overlooked is the overwhelming likelihood that these triumphs in husbandry would not have taken place if man had not also succeeded in domesticating certain wild plants. For only with the luxury of steady surpluses of grains did man have a good chance to provide the time and the food necessary to guarantee the development of domestic strains of animals. It is true, as already noted, that earlier, more primitive societies probably had individual tame or captive animals off and on for thousands of years. But these could not be considered domesticated, since there was little possibility of ensuring a continuing breeding population of any of them—with the exception of the dog, which was a scavenger. Undoubtedly other animal species were caught, kept for a while, then abandoned or eaten—or more probably starved—over and over again until the discovery of agriculture. This made all the difference for both man and beast, and for that reason the taming of plants is considered to be more fundamental to the evolution of human culture than the taming of animals.

The so-called Hilly Crescent, formed by the western foothills of the Zagros

WILD EMMER   AEGILOPS

SPELT   COMMON WHEAT

ANCESTRY OF WHEAT

Plant geneticists believe two wild grasses of the Middle East—wild emmer and Aegilops—were the parents of spelt, once the main wheat of Europe. Not only have the two been found together in ancient sites, but they have been crossed to produce spelt. Common wheat, which has largely replaced spelt, comes from a cross between Aegilops and another primitive wheat. The principal difference between primitive and modern wheats is that the spikes of the former dry and fall apart at maturity, making harvesting difficult. Spelt is less brittle than the old grasses, common wheat the least brittle of all.

Mountains in what is now Iran and Iraq, by the Taurus range of southern Turkey and by the Galilean uplands of northern Palestine, is the area that first saw man's gradual transition from the collecting of wild grains to the deliberate cultivation of their advanced descendants. In this region even today can be found, growing side by side, the three wild prototypes of the first cereals that man succeeded in taming.

These are large-grained wild wheat, small-grained wild wheat and wild barley. The ripened heads of these three wild grasses were probably collected as a sort of iron ration by the pre-Neolithic hunter-gatherers of the Middle East as they passed through grassy regions in quest of game. This random harvest of the hills, the theory goes, would be carried back to the hunters' winter camps in the plains. Inevitably a few handfuls of grain would be spilled, perhaps near a perennial spring or in some spot that received winter and spring rainfall. These lost seeds would root naturally and start a spontaneous plantation. Such a wild garden could scarcely go unnoticed, and perhaps for no other motivation than to avoid the wearying trek up sunburned slopes 2,000 to 4,000 feet high where the wild grass grew, men took deliberately to planting the grass seeds in the level lowlands. Thus in all likelihood was agriculture born: in loads of wild wheat and wild barley grain carried down from their native heights and scattered near a spring somewhere at the foot of the Mesopotamian mountains.

Hans helbaek of the National Museum at Copenhagen, one of the leading experts in this field, points out that one probable result of this human removal of wild grain species from their natural habitat would have been to encourage the survival of mutations—hybrids and freaks that otherwise would have been doomed to extinction. Thus a new sort of natural selection was begun under man's hands, and the biological road that led to today's domestic, large-grained emmer and small-grained einkorn was opened. Nor is all of this pure speculation. Helbaek's careful work at Jarmo has established that not only were the large- and small-grained wild varieties of wheat being cultivated around 6000 B.C., but also barley and a mutation of the large-grained wheat that was already clearly an emmer.

It is from emmer that all the other kinds of cultivated wheat have been derived. Emmer is found in the alluvial plains of lower Iraq from the fifth millennium B.C. onward: it obviously adjusted well to this artificial environment of irrigated land whereas the other wheat mutation, einkorn, did not. By 4000 B.C., both of these domesticated wheats had reached Europe and were being cultivated in the wide loess plains that stretch intermittently almost from the Danube delta to the mouth of the Rhine; by 2000 B.C. wheat agriculture had extended as far as Switzerland, France, northern Italy, Spain, Britain and Scandinavia in the west, and had spread eastward to the Indus valley.

As with wheat, the wild form of barley, with two rows of grain on its head, had not long been grown on irrigated land before a new variety, six-row barley, made its appearance, probably as the result of a mutation. By 4000 B.C. two-row barley had disappeared from the cultivated fields of Mesopotamia and Egypt to be replaced by the six-row variety. Since then, a great many other barley varieties, capable of growth in a wide variety of climates, have developed. Today this cereal is cultivated from the Equator to the North Cape and from Ireland to Japan. Its distribution is as extreme in altitude as it is in latitude—from 1,100 feet below sea level in the Dead Sea region to some 12,000 feet above sea level in the Himalayas.

OATS   RYE

ANCESTRY OF OATS AND RYE

Both these plants were first developed from certain weeds found growing in wheat fields and did not come into use as domestic crops until considerably later than wheat did—3,000 years ago for oats, 2,000 years ago for rye. Although they have been losing ground to wheat in recent centuries, both are still widely grown in Eurasia because they thrive in fields too poor to support wheat. Rye was once the principal grain of Europe. It still yields more human food per acre at a lower cost than any other. Oats are grown today mainly as livestock feed, since rye is not as good for animals.

Some of the other modern cereal crops were first introduced into Europe as lowly weeds that grew up amidst the wheat. This is the case with both oats and rye. The first probably came from the Near East or eastern Europe, the second from the western part of central Asia. Oats did not reach the status of a crop plant before 1000 B.C., while rye was brought into domestication in central Europe barely before the start of the Christian era. Still another cereal, broom-corn millet, appeared for the first time about 3000 B.C. in Mesopotamia, but its progenitor remains unknown. Although millet never had great importance in the Near East, it was widely cultivated in Europe in the second millennium B.C. and has become a major cereal crop in the Far East.

The various wild grasses, although of prime importance, were not the only members of the plant kingdom to be utilized by Neolithic man. By 6000 B.C., the inhabitants of Jarmo were eating such various members of the pea family as the field pea, the lentil and the beach pea, although it is not certain whether these legumes were being cultivated at this time or being gathered wild. In any case, lentils were definitely being grown in Egypt by 3000 B.C. and in Hungary by 2000 B.C., and both field peas and beach peas were known in Switzerland by the latter date. Another legume, the broad bean, appeared around the Mediterranean between 2000 and 1000 B.C. and later spread to most of Europe, arriving in Britain late in the first millennium B.C. Still another legume, the chick pea, makes its appearance in Palestinian finds dating from 3000 B.C.

Vegetable protein, vegetable carbohydrate—what about vegetable fat? The first oil plant deliberately cultivated by man appears to have been flax—sown in the foothills of the Kurdish mountains as early as 4000 B.C. Olives soon followed, showing up in Palestinian and Egyptian finds dating from before 3000 B.C. Other food plants now begin to appear in abundance. The wine grape, which grows wild in some Near Eastern mountain forests, has been cultivated since 3000 B.C. or even earlier, and the date palm appears to have been domesticated at the same time as the olive. Orchards of apples, pears, cherries and figs were apparently unknown west of Greece until the first millennium B.C.

The animals and plants so far mentioned in this chapter might be characterized as the stars of the Neolithic revolutionary drama. But we cannot neglect the many bit players and extras that have followed in their path. For man, in taming the scant dozens of species that provide the bulk of Eurasia's staple foods, has voluntarily or involuntarily brought along with them a considerable number of others. Many of these—not only deliberate introductions but what one might call stowaways as well—have failed to take root. After a few years or a few decades, they either disappeared or found themselves reduced to small colonies on foreign soil. But others, particularly those that found no indigenous competitor or were particularly esteemed by man, have succeeded wonderfully well—sometimes to the point of radically modifying their adopted surroundings.

Some of these now widespread invaders are, quite simply, escapees from captivity. For example, in all of Eurasia at the end of the last glaciation, although hares were widely distributed, the smaller wild rabbit existed only in the Iberian peninsula (and perhaps limited colonies in southern France and the island of Corsica). The first Phoenicians to touch the Spanish coast, around 1100 B.C., were struck by the abundance of this small mammal. The visitors already knew an animal—the hyrax, which they called *shephan*—that lived in groups as did the Spanish rabbits. Thus the Phoenicians named the new territory *i-shephan-im*, a term that (when later latinized as Hispania) gave Spain its present name.

THE ROUNDED HORN OF A WILD GOAT

A clue to the date when goats were first domesticated in the Middle East lies in the shape of the horn core of the male. The small inset drawing (above) shows what a cross section of this goat's horn would look like if cut at the point marked by the straight line. It shows a horn core that is curved on both sides. Since wild goats have horn cores like this, the assumption is that remains found in older strata of prehistoric cultural debris are those of wild animals taken by hunting.

But the wild rabbit was unknown to the Greeks and was not brought to Italy until the First Century B.C., at which time the Romans introduced it into their *leporaria*, those famous walled gardens in which they were already breeding varying hares for the cook pot.

But wild rabbits, unlike hares, are excellent diggers. They managed to escape from the *leporaria* by burrowing under the walls, and it is very likely that these fugitives were the first to populate Italy. The wild rabbit was probably introduced to Great Britain in the same manner during the 12th Century, some 200 to 400 years after the first French attempts to domesticate the species as an additional item of diet in monasteries. Thereafter, rabbit breeding spread throughout the western world. The fact that true domestication was soon achieved is evident from the present wide variety of coat colors (various browns, solid black, and the well-known albino, or "white," rabbits are examples). Color variations are characteristic of domestic animals of all sorts.

For centuries, then, the custom of keeping wild rabbits in enclosures was continued in Europe, and the inevitable escapees slowly populated all the western part of Eurasia. Today the rabbit covers Europe from Gibraltar to the Vistula and from Ireland to Sicily, having failed to colonize only the Alpine plateau and peaks of Switzerland. It is also found in Australia, New Zealand, and such remote spots as Tierra del Fuego and the Falkland Islands, where it has been recently introduced by man.

By the 18th Century the rabbit was a prized European game animal. Two hundred years later it had become a menace. The relentless teeth of millions of rabbits were devouring young seedlings, saplings and shrubs until the undergrowth in many French woodlands looked as though it had been cropped by sheep. The surging rabbit population was halted only by the deliberate introduction in 1952 of a disease, myxomatosis, known to be fatal to rabbits. Its effects were drastic; frequently more than 99 per cent of the population in a district was destroyed. The effect of the rabbit decline on vegetation was just as dramatic; a rapid regeneration of forest undergrowth took place from the Mediterranean to the North Sea.

Another mammal, this one of extra-Eurasian origin, has recently adapted itself to the Palearctic. Three female and two male muskrats were brought from North America to an area near Prague in 1905. From this slender beginning, within 50 years, muskrats have spread all over central Europe, from the Rhine to the Danube and the Volga. Recent muskrat escapees from fur farms have started new centers of population in France and the Low Countries. Since 1927, imported muskrats have prospered in the U.S.S.R., where they may now be found throughout the swampy taiga, from the Baltic to eastern Siberia.

Europe's fresh-water fish population began to be modified in the 18th Century as canals were built connecting various formerly isolated river valleys. Another and more rapid change has occurred in the past 75 years, in part because of deliberate and accidental introductions and in part because the increasing industrial pollution of streams has favored some species and eliminated others. In France, for example, during the last 50 years four North American fishes have increased. The brown bullhead escaped from captivity in Paris in 1871. The common sunfish was introduced in 1886. The large-mouthed black bass has thrived since its introduction in 1880, as has the rainbow trout which was put into French streams at the same time. Two crustaceans have also spread widely. The American crayfish was introduced near Frankfurt in about 1890

THE FLATTENED HORN OF A DOMESTICATED GOAT

In about 7000 B.C. the bones of animals with horn cores that were flat on their inner surface (see cross section, above) began to be killed and eaten by people in Palestine and Mesopotamia. Since domesticated goats have similarly flattened horn cores, experts have concluded that these remains represent animals that had already undergone evolutionary change during the course of domestication. There is no evidence yet as to when or why these changes in horn shape first occurred.

and has gradually spread westward throughout France. The Chinese mitten crab was noticed for the first time in 1912 in a tributary of Germany's Weser River. It has since colonized most continental river mouths from the Baltic to the English Channel.

As for insects, many species—from the American vine aphid and the Colorado potato beetle to the Argentine ant of South America and the cottony-cushion scale insect of Australia—have invaded all parts of Eurasia, often causing widespread crop damage before they found tolerable niches in the artificial biotic communities of agricultural areas. Of course, such invasions are not one-way: the Norway rat, the European starling, the house sparrow, the cabbage worm and the European spruce sawfly are among Eurasia's contributions to the world's agricultural pests.

Eurasia's flora has been even more profoundly affected than its fauna by the importation of exotic plants and by silent infiltration of alien weeds and herbs. In such regions as the French and Italian Riviera, most of the eye-catching trees, shrubs and flowering plants are not native at all but newcomers, sometimes from afar. Both the eucalyptus and the mimosa come from Australia, the florist's geranium and the dew plant from the Cape of Good Hope, and the spike-leafed *Agave* and the prickly-pear cactus from the New World. The bamboo, from China and Japan, is not technically a stranger to Eurasia, but it is certainly an exotic species in western Europe. Nor are these imports mere greenhouse specimens: they thrive out-of-doors, resist the Riviera's occasional frosts and spread beyond garden boundaries to root themselves freely in suitable places along the coast. In the famous Villa Thuret at Antibes, for example, more than 6,000 exotic species out of the 60,000 or so that were tested there during the course of a century have been acclimatized with success.

THIS exotic invasion of the sunny Mediterranean is, of course, the deliberate work of man. But elsewhere in Eurasia, alien species are widely found in the vegetation of prairie and field, of roadside and wasteland. Indeed, no one has yet managed to complete a catalogue of the exotic species now naturalized in western Europe alone. There is hardly any doubt that such a list would total many hundreds of plant intruders from all the temperate zones of the world. Some of them were introduced into western Europe by the first Neolithic cultivators, mixed in among the seeds of useful crops. This is the case with the red poppy, whose seeds have been found among the grains of barley sealed in an Egyptian tomb in 2500 B.C. Other exotics marched north and west along the Roman roads and still others made long sea voyages to Europe, clinging to the hairy bales of imported wool. A surprising total of 348 different species of alien plants, presumably introduced in wool shipments, has been found growing along the banks of Scotland's River Tweed. Of these, 46 per cent originated either in continental Europe or the Near East. But 12 per cent of the alien species were from South Africa, 12 per cent from South America, six per cent from North America and 14 per cent from distant Australia.

Such an example as this underscores the fact that man's 11,000 years of domesticating nature is by no means at an end. The Neolithic revolution brought about multiple and profound changes in Eurasia, a process which has been suddenly accelerated by the industrial revolution of the 19th Century and by the demographic explosion that followed. The end is not yet. This new and largely artificial world is still being shaped, and much of the shaping is taking place without man's consent—even without his knowledge.

A LAPLANDER ROPES A REINDEER, AN ANIMAL THAT WAS DOMESTICATED IN NORTHERN EURASIA PERHAPS AS MUCH AS 8,000 YEARS AGO

What Else Is Tamable?

The surprising thing about the history of domestication is not the large number of animals and plants man uses, but the fact that he does not employ more. All the antelopes, for example, could be domesticated, yet only one is being tamed today—the eland. In some cases, animals can be said to be taming themselves— becoming so used to man that they are now exploiting his world.

A WOMAN OF OUTER MONGOLIA MILKS A REINDEER. HER PEOPLE HAVE TO BE NOMADS, SINCE THEIR REINDEER GO ON SEASONAL MIGRATIONS

The Latest Domesticated Animal

Close by the region where man may have tamed the reindeer, another wild animal has been put to work. It is the European elk, cousin to the American moose. Tamed in the past, it was not domesticated until recently when experiments with elk in the Soviet Union produced tractable animals for use in the taiga and tundra. Captured soon after birth, elk were raised in two- or three-mile-long runs. Wild elk were allowed in to mate with them, and the offspring were bottle-fed and eventually bred. The domesticated elk lacks the reindeer's migratory behavior, needs no stable even in winter, gets along on a diet of twigs, leaves and bark, and can haul 1,100-pound loads at a trot over ice and snow. Moreover, unlike most automotive equipment, it does not get bogged down in the spring and autumn muck of the taiga—its big, splayed hoofs see to that.

MILKING AN ELK, a Soviet wildlife farmhand stands up to her chore. The long-legged elk moves easily through dense brush; political prisoners reportedly used it to escape the Czar's police.

EQUIPPED WITH BRIDLE, BIT AND REINS, A FULL-GROWN ELK SERVES AS A MOUNT FOR A SOVIET FARM GIRL

A HERD OF 50 ELAND AT THE ASKANIYA NOVA EXPERIMENTAL STATION IN THE UKRAINE DATES BACK TO 1896 WHEN AFRICAN STOCK WAS

TAME ORYXES, commemorated in a 4,000-year-old Egyptian painting, seem to have been honored pets of a prince. The Egyptians also domesticated the addax, another big antelope.

A New Kind of Cattle?

Most farm animals descend from Eurasian ancestors. Only a few, like the donkey, are of African origin. But if experiments with the eland succeed, Africa will have made another important contribution. The eland antelope has great potential. It is big and meaty, and the cows produce excellent milk; in the part of Africa where cattle fall victim to the nagana borne by the tsetse fly, the eland thrives. On a farm in the Soviet steppes it has become so tame it allows itself to be milked and even ridden. Attempts to cross it with cattle have been to no avail, but Russian and South African experimenters have not given up, and a truly domesticated eland may yet have the worldwide distribution of *Bos*—the common cow.

IMPORTED. OVER THE YEARS THE ANIMALS HAVE BECOME ACCLIMATED AND GRAZE ON THE STEPPES AS THEY WOULD ON THEIR NATIVE VELD

YOUNG ELAND are fed by a farm assistant. They are especially tame, having been taken from their mothers soon after birth to fix them on humans, first step in the domestication process.

MILK PRODUCER, the eland will yield up to seven and a half quarts. The average butterfat content is 10 per cent, but may be as high as 14 per cent—better than the record for cow milk.

Wild Traits in Tame Species

Although domestication has worked many physical changes on animals, rendering some almost completely different in appearance from their wild ancestors, there are a few that retain many features of the original stock. The double-humped Bactrian camel of Asia (*left*), for example, keeps its wild coloration and size, as does the single-humped dromedary. Both camels, in fact, represent odd choices for domestication. They are slow to breed, foul-smelling and hard to train, and possibly would not have been adopted by man were it not for their value as transports in difficult terrain. Also, unlike most other domesticated animals, they cannot be penned and need extensive pasturage, therefore continuing to live much as they would if they were still wild.

THE BACTRIAN CAMEL bears a close resemblance to the wild species—so much so that some zoologists argue that present wild specimens may be the domesticated breed turned feral.

CAMARGUE BULLS, ROUNDED UP IN FRANCE, SHOW SUCH ANCIENT AUROCHS FEATURES AS HANDLE-BAR HORNS WITH TUFTS BETWEEN THEM

THE SILVER-GRAY OXEN of the Roman countryside are descended from an extinct race of southern cattle. They were established as a breed by Romans before the Christian era.

DOMESTICATED YAKS of central Asia, esteemed as beasts of burden and suppliers of wool, milk and fuel, have undergone color changes, but kept the long, thick hair of the wild species.

MONGOL HORSES ARE PUT OUT TO GRAZE. THOUGH BRED FOR CENTURIES, THEY ARE NOT MUCH BIGGER THAN THEIR PONY-SIZED ANCESTORS

DENSE STANDS OF TREES in Germany's Black Forest contain several imported species. Fast-growing softwoods like North American Douglas fir were introduced in the 19th Century.

Thus, although the area has remained wooded since early times, it has changed considerably in make-up. Where native hardwoods once grew, carefully tended conifers now prevail.

SEED-LADEN SUNFLOWERS weigh down their stalks in the Ukraine. Associated by many people with Russia, sunflowers are actually American and were imported by Russians as potential oil producers. Once the oil is pressed out, the rich seedcake is fed to cattle.

Green Newcomers to the Old World

As great as is man's sway over the animals, it is small in comparison to his domination of the plants. In Eurasia many of the native species have been replaced by imported varieties. This practice has its hazards, especially in regions whose ecological balances have already been upset by man. Thus, the prickly-pear cactus (*below*), after it escaped from cultivated plots, met little competition from indigenous plants and spread widely. Wise selection of foreign species, on the other hand, has turned unproductive land to good use, as in the Black Forest (*opposite*), where untillable hillsides now support valuable stands of pulp-producing conifers.

ESCAPED EXOTICS—an aloe on the Riviera and a prickly-pear cactus in Jordan—grow wild in lands to which they were introduced. The South African aloe came to France as a decorative plant, the American cactus to the Mediterranean region as fruit and fodder.

STORKS, though accustomed to dwelling with man, are inexplicably abandoning their northern haunts. Measures to coax them back include custom-built nests and frog-stocked ponds.

THE BARN OWL has fared better than most owls. It takes up residence near human habitations—in stables, belfries and ruins—and cashes in on the supply of its favorite food—mice.

THE BLUE TIT, shown here about to drink cream off milk, has turned to advantage its habit of shredding papery bark and uses it to rip foil from bottles. It can even lift cardboard tops.

Making the Most of Man

Many animals, confronted with the encroachment of civilization upon their natural habitats, are showing that they can adapt to an unnatural habitat—man's. A few rodents and birds, like the ones shown here, make the point. Perhaps the most amazing example of a bird learning to live with man is that of the blue tit (left). Although widely known today as a cream robber, it has been engaged in its life of crime for a relatively short time. The first recorded case of the early bird getting the cream occurred in 1921, in Great Britain. Some tits have gotten so brazen they even attack unattended bottles in the delivery truck while the milkman makes his morning rounds. Now other species, by associative learning, do the same thing all over northeastern Europe.

BLACK RAT AND SUCCESSOR, the Norway brown rat, flourish in man's shadow. The black rat, which brought plague from Asia, has been displaced by the brown rat, a sewer dweller.

A MAN-MADE ROOF OVER ITS HEAD, A BLACKBIRD PEERS FROM ITS WELL-LIT NEST ON A LONDON STREET

8

The Last Strongholds

EURASIA was the cradle of the modern world. Mankind's two great revolutions took place within its boundaries, the first to be nourished by its fruitful earth and the second to feed upon its abundant mineral wealth. For thousands of years the produce of its farmlands supported the densest human populations ever known; on its stage history's bloodiest conflicts and most brutal clashes of ideologies have been played out. Despite all this, it is noteworthy that the vast realm of the Palearctic is far from being totally disfigured by man's works and deeds—or its animal inhabitants totally exterminated.

Over the last thousand years, not one species of land bird has become extinct, and only one land mammal—the aurochs. In contrast, the North American passenger pigeon, Carolina parakeet and Labrador duck have all been wiped out within the last hundred years. Of course, a number of Eurasian animals have become so perilously few that it has been necessary to breed them in captivity to assure their survival. But other dwindling species have made spectacular comebacks, on their own, within the last 30 years. Although subjected to intensive cultivation for generations, the farmlands of western and central Europe have retained their ancestral fertility. In many of the most highly industrialized and densely populated countries, the forest area is on the increase. How can these contradictions be explained?

First, it must be noted that Eurasia's principal centers of urban civilization lie on the periphery of this enormous land mass. What is more, they always have. Not only the Neolithic revolution of 11,000 years ago, but also the industrial revolution of the last century had its origins along the edges of the Palearctic realm. In between, all the great civilizations of temperate Eurasia developed at the vast continent's two opposite extremities. From its birthplace in the Near East, the art of domestication diffused little by little toward the Nile Valley and the great basins of the Danube and the Indus. From a second point of departure, in north China, these arts also spread to Korea, Japan and Southeast Asia. Thus, the heart of Eurasia remained an almost empty domain, the homeland of a few nomadic herdsmen who from time to time alternately raided their rich sedentary neighbors to the west and to the east.

The concentration of Eurasia's culture and population along its edges is no mystery. The seas and the great rivers have long been mankind's principal avenues of communication. Even as late as the 19th Century, under the impetus of the industrial revolution in Europe, the cities that mushroomed did so close by the English Channel and the shores of the North Sea, where ships could most easily bring raw materials and carry away finished products. This tendency to locate near the great ports of the world was heightened by the fact that those areas were already the most developed with respect to roads and canals and cultivated farmlands—and, of course, they also contained the most people. Furthermore, the rise of industry tended to draw people away from the poorer agricultural regions. In many countries, the least fertile districts were soon drained of their inhabitants as new generations abandoned their ancestral villages and left their family fields untended. Thus it was that many parts of the countryside gradually reverted to their natural state.

During the last 60 years, the pattern has changed, and industrialization has begun to creep into central and eastern Europe and into the depths of Eurasia as well. In the Soviet Union the discovery of rich mineral deposits has been responsible for an entirely new phenomenon—the growth of large industrial complexes in the heart of previously inviolate and sometimes hostile wilderness. But these urban oases are still surrounded by enormous stretches of uninhabited land where the primeval vegetation and wildlife remain almost intact. As a result, the basic pattern of the industrial revolution—urban concentration and the abandonment of marginal lands—remains. And it permits us to see, today, intensely urbanized zones side by side with districts where Eurasia's flora and fauna continue to flourish just as they have for thousands of years.

Long before the 19th Century, a degree of coexistence between man and nature came into being in Europe as an almost accidental by-product of royal whim. In the Middle Ages, the ruling monarchs and the nobility laid down a number of laws designed to preserve the forest and its game for the aristocracy. During Clovis' rule in Gaul (466-511 A.D.), aurochs hunting was entirely reserved to the king. In Poland, Boleslas the Great regulated beaver hunting in the year 1000 A.D., and in 1423 A.D. Ladislas Jagiello not only forbade the felling of yew trees, but also drew up a number of measures to protect his kingdom's deer, wild boar, wild horses and moose. France's modern Stream and Forest Administration had its origin in 1291 A.D. with Philip IV's organization of "Masters of Streams and Forests, examiners, inquirers and reformers."

In Germany, royal and baronial decrees from the Middle Ages onward regulated forest usage and grazing rights, thus protecting these areas from excessive lumbering and their game from poachers. There is no doubt that such measures helped slow down the despoilment of natural habitats in much of Europe.

Still a third factor in preserving a number of Eurasian plant and animal species from extinction is the physical existence of natural refuges in many parts of the continent. A glance at the map, whether in the Near East, western or central Europe or even Japan, shows the presence of abundant mountainous districts, suitable for neither agriculture nor industry. In these thinly peopled zones a number of plants and animals, long gone from the rest of the continent, have not only survived but have even built up populations from which other less fortunate habitats have sometimes been stocked anew. Had Eurasia been one huge monotonous plain from the Pacific to the North Sea, it is more than likely that all its wild fauna would have disappeared long ago.

T HANKS to a variety of circumstances, then, a modest but significant natural capital has been retained in Eurasia right into modern times. It is reasonable to ask whether this privileged situation has much chance of continuing, particularly in view of two new factors that have appeared on the scene. First, the accelerated increase of population, not only in Europe, but in the Near and Far East, now makes the need for food production from all cultivable lands acute. During the 19th Century, emigration allowed a substantial number of people from overcrowded European nations to move into sparsely inhabited regions of North and South America, Australia and Africa. Today, this means of easing European population pressures is virtually gone. The great majority of future Europeans — and Near and Far Easterners as well — will have to make a living on their home continent and the means will have to be found to produce the million or so calories per person per year needed to feed them. Agricultural

POPULATION DENSITY AND HUMAN MIGRATION

This map shows: 1) how many people emigrated from Eurasia during the past century and where they went; 2) how the populations of different countries compare in size today. Migration is shown by small squares, each of which represents a million people leaving a country (black squares) or a million people entering a country (blue squares). Thus, 34 million people have entered the U.S., while 18 million have left Britain and 10 million have left Italy. Present populations are indicated by the distorted sizes of the different countries. The western European nations, being densely populated, are shown here much larger than they would be on a conventional map, whereas Africa, with a sparser population, is smaller than it should be, and thinly populated Canada and Australia are tiny. The teeming lands of the East—China, Japan, the Philippines and Indonesia— are proportionately exaggerated in size.

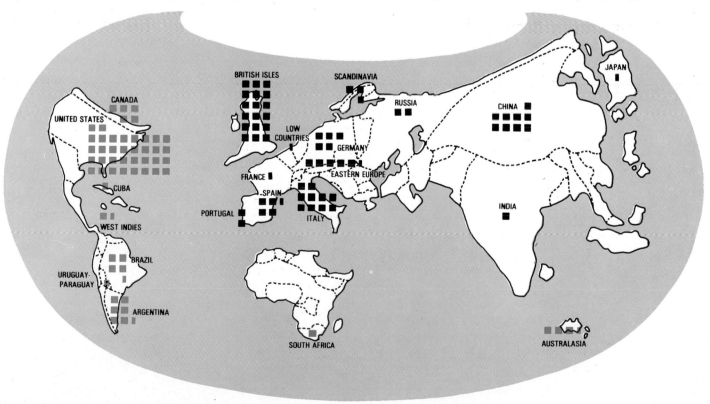

production can be increased in many present farm areas, but these increases will not be enough and it will be impossible to avoid putting abandoned and new lands under cultivation.

The second new factor is mechanical and chemical rather than biological. Although earth-moving equipment has been increasing in efficiency for half a century, we are only now beginning to realize that bulldozers can modify a countryside more thoroughly in 10 years than our ancestors could do in 10 centuries. Today, wherever we look in Eurasia, we see increasingly ambitious irrigation and draining schemes. In central Asia the courses of rivers are being diverted. For thousands of miles trees are being planted in belts to form windbreaks in the open steppe. In some areas the very soil is being modified. All this would have been unheard of three or four generations ago, when man had nothing but his hands, a spade and a plow with which to scratch the earth's skin. Meanwhile chemical weed and insect killers may be sprayed by plane over thousands of square miles. Such chemical agents can irreversibly modify the flora and fauna and help convert to the exclusive benefit of man an ever-increasing proportion of the land's natural productivity. It is clear that never before has mankind possessed such powerful means of harnessing nature—of which, although we tend to forget it, we ourselves are a part.

Taking into account both the positive and the negative aspects of the present situation, what does the future hold for the wildlife of Eurasia? Can there be any policy for the preservation of nature that is compatible with the demographic and economic future of the continent? Let us admit at once that a simple answer to this question does not exist. Any policy of preservation will have to take into account the different economies of Eurasia's various regions, the traditional attitudes of each region's inhabitants toward nature, and the characteristics not only of individual localities, but also of the kinds of wildlife it is hoped to preserve. The problem must be considered separately for urban and industrial zones, for agricultural zones and for those zones that, economically speaking, are marginal. Any effort to teach conservation to the public can scarcely be undertaken in the same way in the north, south and west of Europe, let alone in the Near East or the Orient. Nor can the same techniques of conservation be employed to ensure the survival of a species of insect, a migratory bird and a game mammal. In examining this complex question, let us take into account the various conservation experiments—successful and unsuccessful—that have been carried out in the last few decades.

I N Eurasia's urban and industrial regions, the environment has been largely an artificial one for several generations, and a number of animal and plant species are now remarkably well adapted to this type of life. In the north of Europe whole groups of plants and animals flourish in hedgerows, along railways and embankments and even in slag heaps and dumps. Some of the animals—insects, spiders, snails, worms and even rats—have adapted to such special environments as mine galleries, sewers and canals. A number of small birds have found a habitat suitable to their needs in the parks and tree-lined avenues and even in the stone façades of large towns and cities. These integrated animals have practically nothing to fear from the future. Unfortunately they are only a fraction of the populations these regions supported in preindustrial times.

The present fauna and flora of Eurasia's agricultural districts are not by any means as impoverished as those of the urban-industrial complexes. But their future prospects are bleak. There is no doubt that, as the human population

PARKS AND RESERVES

Eurasia's major nations are ranked below according to the percentage of total area held under government protection in parks and reserves in 1962. Fourth in rank, the United States has been included here for purposes of comparison.

Nation	Total Area (Sq. Miles)	Protected Land
Japan	142,600	6.460%
United Kingdom	94,500	5.288
Czechoslovakia	49,400	3.357
United States	3,615,200	3.213
Austria	32,400	2.779
East Germany	41,600	1.454
Holland	15,800	1.209
Israel	8,000	1.026
West Germany	95,900	.991
Sweden	173,400	.937
Denmark	16,600	.814
Yugoslavia	98,800	.718
Luxembourg	1,000	.656
Italy	116,400	.653
Switzerland	15,900	.507
Albania	10,600	.405
Poland	120,400	.330
U.S.S.R.	8,599,800	.315
Finland	130,200	.311
Romania	91,600	.302
Norway	125,100	.178
Tunisia	48,400	.123
Mongolia	580,100	.122
Spain	194,400	.089
France	213,000	.089
Morocco	172,100	.082
Belgium	11,800	.080
Pakistan	364,700	.073
Eire	27,100	.065
Hungary	35,900	.058
Greece	51,800	.044
Iceland	39,800	.039
Bulgaria	42,800	.026
Algeria	919,600	.011
Turkey	296,500	.007
Bhutan	19,300	none
Iran	628,000	none
Iraq	171,600	none

For the following 11 countries no official information is available: Afghanistan, China, Jordan, Lebanon, Nepal, North Korea, Portugal, Saudi Arabia, Sikkim, South Korea, Syria.

multiplies giddily, all the land capable of producing foodstuffs will sooner or later be tilled and Eurasia's arable acres will be transformed into a sort of Gargantuan calorie factory. On the day that man is faced with the alternative of his own survival or the survival of any wild plant or animal not of direct use to him, there can be no doubt concerning his choice. Nor can anyone blame him: as the British ecologist Charles Elton put it, "It is no use pretending that conservation for pleasure or instruction or the assigning of superior rights to animals will ever take precedence over human survival."

ALREADY, throughout Eurasia's richest countryside, nearly all of man's undesirable wild competitors have been exterminated. Each year, the consolidation of farmland into bigger and bigger units, not to mention the mechanization of field labor and the tendency to plant thousands of acres to a single crop, does away with the hedges, lanes, thickets and ponds that are the last refuges of wildlife in agricultural regions. Everywhere, to facilitate the work of machines, the land is smoothed and leveled. The end is a uniform landscape.

What, then, can be done to save some bits of primeval countryside, to ensure the continuation of breeding or nesting colonies of wild animals? So far, one solution only has proved valid: the setting up of special sanctuaries. This has already been done on a fairly large scale in some countries of Europe, although the percentage of total area that has been allocated to parks is pitifully small, as the table on page 176 shows. In England, Scotland and Wales a remarkable organization, the Nature Conservancy, oversees 95 national nature reserves. The size of these protected zones varies considerably—from as little as four to nearly 40,000 acres, but the majority of them are small, as are a number of bird sanctuaries scattered throughout Great Britain. Holland, in spite of its small size and its dense population, maintains more than 200 nature reserves within its borders. In 1961, West Germany had 750 reserves and Poland 366, of which 86 were solely botanical and 35 were wildlife refuges.

Even small reserves are sometimes spectacularly successful. The Farne Islands, off Great Britain's Northumberland coast, were turned into a bird sanctuary by the National Trust in 1924. Today, these islands are famous for their colonies of terns, guillemots, puffins, kittiwakes, cormorants and common eiders. But the animal that has benefited the most is not a bird at all. For this sanctuary also serves as a breeding ground for the gray seal, 50 years ago one of the rarest seals in the world. Centuries of pitiless hunting had reduced its numbers until, in 1910, only a hundred were to be counted on the little archipelago. In 1938, the official count was still no more than 150 to 200, but by 1950 it had increased to 1,300, and by 1962 to more than 3,500. Now British conservationists must cull the young pups, cutting their numbers back to 750 each year in order to limit the damage the gray seals do to neighboring salmon fisheries.

These figures must be taken with a grain of salt. To begin with, methods of counting have improved a great deal since the earlier seal censuses were taken. Originally sight counts were made by observers on the island or in boats, and it is doubtful if these methods ever succeeded in getting a full count of the population. Today enlargements of photographs made by airplane can be studied in the laboratory and a much more accurate count made. Furthermore, there is some suspicion that protection of the Farne Islands has made it increasingly attractive to immigrant seals who have moved over from the Norwegian coast, where no protection is given them. Despite these factors, which would dilute the figures in the previous paragraph, there is no question that the gray seal population has grown a great deal and that the outlook for the species is vastly improved by the establishment of an island sanctuary where it can breed in peace indefinitely—or until man decides that he needs the Farne Islands for a rocket-launching site or a resort, in which case the seals might well disappear almost overnight.

Important as small hand-tended sanctuaries are, it is in Eurasia's marginal lands that the bulk of the continent's wildlife can and must be saved. High mountains and desert, tundra and taiga have never been hospitable dwelling places for man, and their human population has always been sparse. Such economically valueless regions have served as natural refuges for centuries.

In Europe, as we have already seen, the population of marginal lands has tended to decrease as industrialization has developed. In Corsica and in some alpine regions, for example, the inhabitants have been steadily emigrating for over a century despite all efforts to halt the exodus. Those that do not leave tend to concentrate in a few spots. The growing tourist and winter sports industry has brought about a complete change in the economy of some central European mountain districts; the inhabitants have given up their flocks and lonely valleys to gather in resort areas and serve the holidaymakers. As a result, alpine meadows, emptied of cattle, are undergoing a change in vegetation, and the wild alpine plants already seem to have benefited.

Here is an opportunity that cannot be neglected by any who wish to preserve nature: it should now be possible, at little cost, to create new forest reserves and even great national parks. What is more, as the wilderness restores itself, parts of these sanctuaries could be set aside for hunting, fishing and camping and thus further aid the local economy. As urban Europe grows, the more its citizens will appreciate holiday nights free from noise, air untainted with exhaust fumes and the simple joys of the outdoors. The increasing popularity of camping in Europe since World War II already provides striking proof of this.

ALL things considered, it is scarcely surprising that many of the national parks already established in Eurasia are to be found in marginal areas, and particularly in mountain districts. Italy has four national reserves, all of which are in the mountains. The same is true of Switzerland's one, Spain's five, Yugoslavia's 12, Czechoslovakia's two, and Greece's one. Five of Poland's nine, and seven of Sweden's 15 are mountain parks. The Soviet Union, with 93 national parks and reserves, has located 25 of them in the Urals, the Caucasus, the Altai, the Tien-Shan and various other lofty regions of central and northeast Asia. In Japan the score is 14 out of 19. All in all, an encouraging picture from the viewpoint of mountain plants and animals, particularly if one adds the forest preserves that have been established in the mountains of many countries.

Equally favorable is the situation in the tundra and taiga of Scandinavia and the U.S.S.R. Both Russia and Sweden have been foresighted in the establishment of generous reserves in their northern lands. This, together with the aforementioned existence of extremely large tracts as yet undisturbed by man, makes the outlook for northern flora and fauna generally good.

The steppes and deserts of central Eurasia, by their very vastness, might seem to offer the same sort of inexhaustible natural refuge. But this is far from being the case. In all the earth's temperate latitude no other marginal zone has been so much the object of recent exploitation, much of it in the past decade. All along the northern margin of the U.S.S.R.'s steppe corridor, former prairie is being transformed into farmland, and it is now the turn of central Asia's desert to be put to similar use. Large-scale irrigation works are in progress, and even in the sandy zones of Uzbekistan and Turkmenistan thornless varieties of cactus are being planted as animal fodder.

There is no doubt that a century from now these regions will be transformed and that the plants and animals of steppe and desert, if they survive at all, will do so only in parks and reserves. A few parks already exist, the most important being in Turkmenistan along the Afghan frontier. It is a refuge for the kulan, the leopard and that distinctive, tassel-eared wildcat, the caracal. There are also Soviet parks in Tadzhikistan, in Kazakhstan and in Georgia, plus a few botanical reserves and small refuges farther north to preserve samples of Eurasian prairie vegetation. However, these efforts are inadequate. Many steppe and desert animals, especially the larger ones, are very wide-ranging. Unless governments are willing to gamble with the future of these animals, the number and size of sanctuaries in the steppe corridor must be increased.

EVEN more serious is the outlook for the deciduous forest zone. Subjected to clearing and exploitation for centuries, only rare stretches of this once enormous belt still remain intact. The finest stand surviving in Europe is certainly the famous Bialowieza forest, on the Russo-Polish frontier. This is now fortunately a national park on both sides of the border. At the other end of the continent, the Soviet forest reserves of Primorye provide excellent protection in the Amur region. As for all the rest, from the oak groves of Celtic France to the shaded hills of Confucian China, the former forest is now vanishing.

In the Mediterranean basin, the situation is, if anything, worse. There is a great need for a better protection of the various sorts of forests that typify this life zone, or of the interesting fauna that thrive there. Although a few forest reserves supposedly serve this purpose, they are inadequately patrolled and all too often scarred by catastrophic fires started by careless campers. These reserves could be made useful if they were transformed into national parks with proper surveillance and management. The protection of many Mediterranean islands that are still largely free from human activity would be equally rewarding. The case of Port Cros, in the Hyères archipelago off the French coast, provides an encouraging example. Here, a remarkable specimen of the primeval western Mediterranean forest has been preserved intact only a few miles from the most densely populated regions of the Côte d'Azur.

In Europe, at least, the most critically threatened environment of all is the wetland—the habitat of marsh and pond. In agricultural and industrial regions alike these watery spots have been subject to drainage and reclamation for the last two centuries, and have now virtually disappeared. The loss of this type of environment affects much more than a specialized group of swamp and water plants. It is equally disastrous for a great variety of migratory waterfowl and wading birds that require wetlands as resting points during their spring and autumn journeys, and also in many cases as wintering places.

Here the interests of hunter and naturalist are identical. It was in order to facilitate common action that the International Union for the Conservation of Nature and Natural Resources in 1962 undertook an inventory of the wetlands of western Europe and North Africa to determine which should be made into reserves to assure the future of many bird species. This inventory brought to light the unbelievable depletion of wetland habitat in western Europe. Even taking into account lagoons, coastal marshes, stretches of fresh water, swamps and bogs, the number of major habitats for aquatic birds in each country is frighteningly small. For example, there are only six in Great Britain, five each in France and Holland, four in Germany, three each in Italy and Sweden, two each in Norway and Switzerland and only one in Portugal.

A few of these key wetlands are already protected more or less effectively and permanently, but this is far from the case generally and some of the unguarded regions may be drained in the very near future. The situation is particularly critical in southern Europe and in North Africa. The three most famous marshes —the Marismas of the Guadalquivir River in Spain, the Camargue of France and the Danube delta in the Black Sea—enjoy protection, wholly or in part, but their future is far from being assured. Neither governments nor individual citizens seem to realize that scientific management of such areas brings a better profit from hunters and fishermen in the long run than drainage and farming.

A fundamental difficulty in working out large-scale conservation programs is that the traditional attitude of man towards nature is not the same everywhere. Even within western Europe the public attitude in England, Scandinavia, Holland and Germany is quite different from that in Portugal, Spain, Italy and much of France. In the former countries, there is a traditional sympathy for wildlife: there, when men create a park or garden, it delights them to reproduce the natural landscape more or less faithfully. They let trees and bushes grow freely and even give mass plantings of flowers the subtle air of growing wild. In the Latin countries of Europe, however, man's handiwork is always considered more worthy of interest than nature's. In an Italian or French garden, plants— like statues and fountains—are considered mere decorative adjuncts, to be arranged in symmetrical and conventional order. Trees and bushes are clipped, often in a manner as little like nature as can be. The wild animals, in turn, are regarded as nothing but pests or potential game. At the other end of Eurasia, a similar divergence is to be seen between China and Japan, while in the Islamic world the pre-eminence of human works in the cultural scale of values is perhaps even more marked than in Latin Europe. Campaigns to educate public opinion must take account of these facts.

IT would be unrealistic to think that nature can be saved against the will of man. His assent and active cooperation are absolutely necessary. Yet, paradoxically enough, the living creature whose future is the most threatened at the moment is urban and industrial man himself. Historically, all men are only a few hundred generations removed from the hunter's way of life. They are not yet adapted either physically or mentally to modern civilization's artificial surroundings, with their breakneck pace of life, intense competition, incessant noise and pollution of every kind. It is little wonder that, in spite of the progress of medicine and a rise in the standard of living, man finds himself a prey to a whole series of fresh ailments which some euphemistically term "diseases of civilization." The antidote to these ills of our times is not going to be provided solely by psychiatry and tranquilizers. A happier balance is also possible between work and rest, between intellectual activity and muscular exercise, between pavement gray and forest green. This possibility is beginning to make its impression on people around the world. There is a preoccupation, be it in Paris or Moscow, Stockholm or Tokyo, with city parks and gardens, with green belts circling industrial centers. Perhaps the greatest and best hope for the cause of conservation both in Eurasia and in other threatened realms throughout the world is the increasing realization that man is not built to spend his whole life in a universe of steel and concrete.

A STONE WARRIOR STANDS OUTSIDE PEKING BY A GRAIN FIELD THAT HAS BEEN CONTINUOUSLY CULTIVATED SINCE THE MING DYNASTY

Man against the Land

Until Stone Age man succeeded in growing crops and taming animals, all his time was spent hunting food. His effect on the land was negligible. But once he settled down and began to dig and dam and drain, he set in motion a process that—for good or ill—has been gathering force for several thousand years. Today he has the choice of wrecking the earth or learning to live in harmony with it.

181

UNDER A RUINED AQUEDUCT near Rome springs a field of rye. This land was almost destroyed through 2,000 years of abuse, but is being brought back into good production.

Lands That Still Yield, Despite Long Abuse

Much of the world's soil is extraordinarily resilient and, if given half a chance, it will yield generously for man indefinitely. The Greeks and Romans, knowing little about soil conservation and having the double misfortune of living in rather poor arid country, which was also very steep, watched their once-fertile fields not only wash off into the sea, but become depleted from too intensive planting. As a result, a field like the one above was probably exhausted before the time of Christ; the Romans had to import food from distant provinces. And yet a little fertilizer and some water now and then—plus a much-needed rest during the turmoil following barbarian invasions—have kept this field going. Modern agricultural methods are now improving the yields of many depleted areas in Italy and Greece.

IN A DRY VALLEY in Afghanistan, fields of grain grow, thanks to crop rotation, just as they have since the Fourth Century. Holes in the cliffs are cells cut by Buddhist monks.

HOLLOWED OUT LIKE BEEHIVES, ROCKY EXCRESCENCES IN ANATOLIA WERE FIRST INHABITED BY CHRISTIAN MONKS, LATER BY TURKISH FARMERS

A BUDDHIST TEMPLE of the Fifth Century A.D. is carved into a stone cliff in Shansi Province, China. After the temple faded as an active religious center, peasants moved into it.

Soft Rocks and Lofty Ones

Man's use of the land goes well beyond his need for food. Its varying contours and consistencies have long supplied him with dwellings, fortresses and even temples. Pinnacles have always been easily defensible, and for centuries religious groups in lands ravaged by war and brigandage have hidden away in eyries like that shown on the opposite page. In many places the very softness of the rock has invited excavation. The Anatolian plateau in central Turkey contains large flows of soft lava from ancient volcanoes eroded today into free-standing cones and pyramids. Christian holy men first began hollowing them out in 800 A.D. Today some of them are 10 stories high inside and contain dozens of rooms.

A GREEK MONASTERY sits atop an 1,800-foot pinnacle in Thessaly. Visitors can now reach it by steep steps cut in the rock, but in past centuries they were hauled up in string nets.

Of Dikes and Terraces

Over the centuries, men have resorted to all sorts of ingenious ways of gaining more land on which to grow essential food. One of the most dramatic examples is the efforts of the Dutch against the encroaching sea—a battle that has been going on systematically for more than 800 years. Today many of the Netherlands' finest farms flourish as much as 25 feet below sea level, and were it not for the 2,000-mile-long system which links dunes, dikes, dams, sluices and pumps, 40 per cent of the country would now be under water.

Terracing is another way of increasing scarce farmland. As far back as the Bronze Age, men created flat areas of arable land on the slopes of mountains by building low embankments. In Asia 35 centuries ago, farmers in China's Yangtze Valley terraced at 10,000-foot heights in terrain so steep that they climbed ropes to reach their tiny plots. Even today in Szechwan, each crumb of topsoil is so valuable that it is collected in valleys and carried to high terraces on the backs of human laborers.

TIERS OF TERRACES surround the Church of St. Stephano on the island of Sifnos in Greece. Laborious husbandry of these hilly slopes yields the best olive oil in the Greek islands.

A DUTCH DIKE holds back the light-colored salt water of the North Sea (*left*). All the land to the right of the dike is below sea level; the brown section is land that has just been drained.

Gardens and Sanctuaries

Defining man's use of land solely in terms of utilitarian needs fails to account for his aesthetic values or the wide range of his imagination. Land in ancient China 3,000 years ago was turned into gardens for contemplation, expressing the religious belief that man was a part of nature and not a lord over it. Out of an attitude like this eventually came man's recognition that he had a responsibility to plants and animals whose destiny was bound up with his own. Perhaps the first attempt at conservation was the royal parks, where game was bred. But not until recently did he do more to preserve species other than his own. Now, there is hardly a nation that does not offer its wildlife some sort of refuge.

ROOSTING GANNETS cluster thickly at their sanctuary on the Welsh island of Grassholm, one of Great Britain's 95 nature reserves. The island of 21 acres supports 20,000 gannets.

RIPPLES OF MOSS and rock in Kyoto's Moss Temple were laid out over 600 years ago by a Zen Buddhist priest. The garden symbolized the movement toward supreme wisdom.

AGAINST A BACKDROP of clouds an axis deer stands alert in Sikkim's Royal Deer Park. This 5,000-foot-high refuge houses only hardy Himalayan animals that can withstand the cold.

Credits

Credits for pictures from left to right are separated by commas, top to bottom by dashes.

Cover—James Burke
8, 9—Ralph Morse
10—map by Matt Greene
11—maps by Adolph E. Brotman
12—chart by Otto van Eersel
13—drawings by Rudolf Freund
14—Adolph E. Brotman
17—Romain Robert
18, 19—Leo and Diane Dillon
20, 21—James Whitmore courtesy Department of Antiquities, Government of Egypt—Larry Burrows courtesy National Museum Athens, Larry Burrows courtesy Heraclion Archaeological Museum, Crete, Greece
22, 23—Lee Boltin courtesy The Metropolitan Museum of Art: Fletcher Fund; 1931—Lee Boltin courtesy The Metropolitan Museum of Art; Dick Fund; 1954, Larry Burrows courtesy Museo Civico, Brescia, Italy
24, 25—courtesy Bibliothèque Nationale, Paris, Fernand Bourges courtesy The Metropolitan Museum of Art
26—Lee Boltin courtesy The Metropolitan Museum of Art; Rogers Fund, 1947
27—Lee Boltin courtesy The Metropolitan Museum of Art; Purchase 1959 Joseph Pulitzer Bequest—Larry Burrows courtesy Trustees of the British Museum
28, 29—Sabine Weiss from Rapho-Guillumette courtesy The Hermitage Museum, Leningrad
30, 31—Henry B. Beville courtesy Palace Museum Collection
32—Stephanie Dinkins
33, 34—maps by Matt Greene
35—drawings by Peg Estey
36—drawing by Matt Greene
41—drawing by Matt Greene
43—Dmitri Kessel
44, 45—James Burke courtesy The American Museum of Natural History
46, 47—courtesy The American Museum of Natural History—courtesy Natural History

Museum London, The Bettmann Archive, courtesy Arnold Arboretum, Ernst Schäfer
48—New York Zoological Society Photo—Jean Rasmussen
49—courtesy World Book Encyclopedia
50—Lawrence Swan, James Milledge—Lawrence Swan, Richard Marlin Perkins—Richard Marlin Perkins all property of World Book Encyclopedia except left center
51—Lawrence Swan, Richard Marlin Perkins—Lawrence Swan, Richard Marlin Perkins—Richard Marlin Perkins, Lawrence Swan all property of World Book Encyclopedia
52 through 55—Joseph Cellini
56—Roger C. Bell from Photo Researchers, Inc.
57—map by Matt Greene
58, 59—drawings by Jack Kunz
60—drawings by Otto van Eersel
62—drawing by Otto van Eersel
65—Stephanie Dinkins
66, 67—François Bourlière, Dmitri Kessel
68—François Bourlière—Karl Weber & Heinz Hafner, Eric Hosking from Photo Researchers, Inc. (2)—Patrick Synge, François Bourlière (2)
69—David Douglas Duncan—Arabian American Oil Co.
70—Schinasi from Monkmeyer Press Photos—David Douglas Duncan
71—David Douglas Duncan
72, 73—James Burke
74, 75—left Lies Wiegman; right Lee Talbot—W. Suschitzky, New York Zoological Society
76—Ralph Crane
77, 78—Eric Hosking from Photo Researchers, Inc.
79—Karl Weber & Heinz Hafner
80—James Burke
81—map by Matt Greene
83—drawings by Peg Estey
84—map by Matt Greene
85—courtesy L. Carrington

Goodrich—The Bettmann Archive
87—drawings by Peg Estey
89—map by Matt Greene
91—Eastfoto
92, 93—James Burke
94, 95—David Douglas Duncan
96—William Vandivert
97—Lisa Larsen except bottom Jorgen Bisch from Pix Inc.
98, 99—Stephanie Dinkins
100, 101—Paul Furse except bottom right Patrick Synge
102—Tierbilder Okapia; Frankfurt/Main—W. Gewalt
103—W. Suschitzky
104, 105—E. P. Gee
106—Helmut Heimpel
107—map by Matt Greene
108—charts by John Newcomb
110, 111—Matt Greene
112, 113—Rudolf Freund
115—Hans Lidman
116, 117—Helmut Heimpel
118—courtesy Zoological Society of London
119—Russ Kinne from Photo Researchers, Inc.
120, 121—Marvin E. Newman, John Markham
122, 123—Makoto Ito, John Markham—Aldo Margiocco, Russ Kinne from Photo Researchers, Inc.
124, 125—Aldo Margiocco
126—Oscar Schmid from Photo Researchers, Inc.
127—Pictorial Parade, John Markham—Wlodzimierz Puchalski
128, 129—"Images et Textes": F. Merlet
130, 131—Karl Gullers from Rapho-Guillumette—map by Matt Greene
134—drawing by Jack Kunz
135—drawing by Peg Estey
137—map by Otto van Eersel
139—Sven Gillsäter
140, 141—Hans Lidman except top left Sven Gillsäter
142, 143—Nystrand from Annan Photo Features
144, 145—N. R. Farbman except top right Fritz Henle from

Photo Researchers, Inc.
146—Mauno Mannelin
147—William C. Steere courtesy The New York Botanical Garden—Oskar Dorfmann, Toni Schneiders from Photo Researchers, Inc.
148, 149—Jan Lindblad from Photo Researchers, Inc.
150—Howard Sochurek
152, 153—drawings by Jack Kunz
154—chart by John Newcomb
156 through 159—Rudolf Freund
161—Keystone Press Agency
162—Howard Sochurek—Herbert Scheifler
163—Herbert Scheifler
164, 165—Herbert Scheifler—courtesy The Oriental Institute of the University of Chicago, N. W. Lobanow (2)
166—Jorgen Bisch from Pix Inc.—Hans W. Silvester from Rapho-Guillumette
167—Lee Talbot, Douglas Scott—Lisa Larsen
168, 169—Lee Talbot, Howard Sochurek—A. L. Goldman from Rapho-Guillumette, Dmitri Kessel
170—Roger Tory Peterson from The Audubon Society, Heinz Tomanek from Photo Researchers, Inc.—John Markham, Jane Burton from Photo Researchers, Inc., Freelance Photographers Guild
171—*Paris-Match*
172—Stephanie Dinkins
175—Matt Greene courtesy The Twentieth Century Fund
181—Tom Hutchins
182, 183—Ralph Crane, Stephanie Dinkins from Photo Researchers, Inc.
184—Marc Riboud from Magnum Photos—Tom Hutchins
185—Dmitri Kessel
186, 187—Bart Hofmeester Rotterdam, Dmitri Kessel
188—Eric Hosking—David Douglas Duncan
189—Stephanie Dinkins
192, 193—map by Bill Dove

Acknowledgments

The editors of this book are particularly indebted to Charles Vaurie, Associate Curator, Department of Ornithology, The American Museum of Natural History, who read the text in its entirety. They also want to thank Elizabeth Bacon; Elso S. Barghoorn, Professor of Botany, Harvard University; Rupert Barneby, Honorary Curator, New York Botanical Garden; William Dwight Billings, Professor of Botany, Duke University; Stanley A. Cain, Professor of Botany, University of Michigan; John H. Callen, Field Enterprises Educational Corporation; Edwin H. Colbert, Chairman and Curator, Department of Vertebrate Paleontology, The American Museum of Natural History; William G. Conway, Director, New York Zoological Park; Harold J. Coolidge, Chairman, American Committee for International Wild Life Protection, Washington, D.C.; Arthur Cronquist, Senior Curator, New York Botanical Garden; Mabel A. Cronquist, Librarian, Horticultural Society of New York; Robert L. Edwards, Assistant Director, Biological Laboratory, U.S. Bureau of Commercial Fisheries, Woods Hole, Mass.; Eugene Eisenmann, Research Associate, Department of Ornithology, The American Museum of Natural History; L. Carrington Goodrich, Professor Emeritus of Chinese, Columbia University; Calvin J. Heusser, Research Associate in Palynology, American Geographic Society; Sidney Horenstein, Scientific Assistant, Department of Fossil Invertebrates, The American Museum of Natural History; C. T. Hu, Professor of Education, Teachers College, Columbia University; Richard M.

Klein, Curator of Plant Physiology, New York Botanical Garden; Thorkild Jacobsen, Visiting Professor of Assyriology, Harvard University; Quentin Jones, Plant Industries Division, U.S. Department of Agriculture; Malcolm McKenna, Assistant Curator, Department of Vertebrate Paleontology, The American Museum of Natural History; William G. Merrill, Assistant Professor of Animal Husbandry, Cornell University; Fairfield Osborn, President, New York Zoological Society; William S. Osburn Jr., Associate Director, Institute of Arctic and Alpine Research, University of Colorado; William O. Pruitt, Department of Zoology, University of Oklahoma; Charles A. Reed, Professor of Zoology, Yale University; Jerome G. Rozen, Chairman and Associate Curator, Department of Entomology, The American Museum of Natural History; Phyllis Barclay Smith, British Museum of Natural History, London; William Campbell Steere, Director, New York Botanical Garden; Lawrence W. Swan, Associate Professor of Biology, San Francisco State College; Professor A. A. Toschi, Laboratorio de Zoologia Applicata alla Caccia, Bologna, Italy; Richard G. Van Gelder, Chairman and Associate Curator, Department of Mammalogy, The American Museum of Natural History; Constance H. Young; Richard G. Zweifel, Curator of Herpetology, The American Museum of Natural History; The American Committee of International Wild Life Protection; the library staffs of The American Museum of Natural History and the New York Botanical Garden.

Appendix

Common and Scientific Names of Eurasian Animals

To make this book as useful as possible to the general reader, the animals mentioned in the text have been referred to, where possible, by their common names. However, since common names may vary from place to place, this list has been prepared so that students can identify them positively by their scientific names. Some of the commonest have been omitted, as well as a few for which there was no space. Two animals with identical scientific names are varieties of one species.

Mammals

antelope, Tibetan, or chiru   *Pantholops hodgsoni*
ape, Barbary   *Macaca sylvana*
argali, or great Tibetan sheep   *Ovis ammon*
aurochs   *Bos primigenius*
badger   *Meles meles*
bat, greater horseshoe   *Rhinolophus ferrumequinum*
bear, brown   *Ursus arctos*
beaver, European   *Castor fiber*
bison, European   *Bison bonasus*
boar, wild   *Sus scrofa*
camel, Bactrian   *Camelus bactrianus*
caracal   *Felis caracal*
chamois   *Rupicapra rupicapra*
cheetah   *Acinonyx jubatus*
chipmunk, Siberian   *Tamias sibiricus*
deer, axis, or chital   *Axis axis*
deer, fallow   *Dama dama*
deer, musk   *Moschus moschiferus*
deer, Père David's   *Elaphurus davidianus*
deer, Persian fallow   *Dama mesopotamica*
deer, red   *Cervus elaphus*
deer, roe   *Capreolus capreolus*
deer, sika   *Cervus nippon*
dormouse, fat   *Glis glis*
elk, European, or moose   *Alces alces*
fox, arctic   *Alopex lagopus*
fox, corsac   *Vulpes corsac*
fox, red   *Vulpes vulpes*
fox, Tibetan sand   *Vulpes ferrilata*
gazelle, goitered   *Gazella subgutturosa*
gazelle, Tibetan   *Procapra picticaudata*
goat, wild   *Capra hircus*
goral   *Nemorhaedus goral*
hare, European   *Lepus europaeus*
hare, mountain or varying   *Lepus timidus*
horse, Przewalski's   *Equus przewalskii*
hyena, striped   *Hyaena hyaena*
hyrax   *Procavia capensis*
ibex   *Capra ibex*
ibex, Spanish   *Capra pyrenaica*
jackal, Asiatic   *Canis aureus*
jerboa, great   *Allactaga major*
kiang, or Tibetan wild ass   *Equus hemionus*
kulan, or Mongolian wild ass   *Equus hemionus*
lemming, Norway   *Lemmus lemmus*
leopard   *Leo pardus*
lion   *Leo leo*
lynx   *Lynx lynx*
macaque, Japanese   *Macaca fuscata*
markhor, or wild goat   *Capra falconeri*
marmot, alpine   *Marmota marmota*
marmot, bobac   *Marmota bobak*
marten, pine   *Martes martes*
mole rat, Russian   *Spalax microphthalmus*
mole-vole, northern   *Ellobius talpinus*
monkey, snub-nosed   *Rhinopithecus roxellanae*
mouflon   *Ovis musimon*
mouflon, Asiatic   *Ovis orientalis*
onager, or Persian wild ass   *Equus hemionus*
oryx   *Oryx tao*
otter   *Lutra lutra*
panda, giant   *Ailuropoda melanoleuca*
panda, lesser   *Ailurus fulgens*

pika, daurian   *Ochotona daurica*
polecat   *Mustela putorius*
rabbit   *Oryctolagus cuniculus*
rat, black   *Rattus rattus*
rat, Norway   *Rattus norvegicus*
reindeer, or caribou   *Rangifer tarandus*
sable   *Martes zibellina*
seal, Baikal, or nerpa   *Phoca sibirica*
seal, Caspian   *Phoca caspica*
seal, gray   *Halichoerus grypus*
seal, Mediterranean monk   *Monachus monachus*
seal, ringed   *Phoca hispida*
sheep, Barbary   *Ammotragus lervia*
sheep, blue, or bharal   *Pseudois nayaur*
sheep, Marco Polo's   *Ovis ammon*
shrew, alpine   *Sorex alpinus*
squirrel, Russian flying   *Pteromys volans*
takin   *Budorcas taxicolor*
tiger   *Panthera tigris*
tur, Caucasian   *Capra caucasica*
vole, field   *Microtus agrestis*
wapiti, Manchurian   *Cervus elaphus*
weasel   *Mustela nivalis*
wild ass, Asiatic   *Equus hemionus*
wild cat, African   *Felis libyca*
wild cat, European   *Felis silvestris*
wolf   *Canis lupus*
wolverine   *Gulo gulo*
yak, wild   *Bos grunniens*

Birds

accentor, alpine   *Prunella collaris*
bee eater, common   *Merops apiaster*
blackbird   *Turdus merula*
bustard, great   *Otis tarda*
bustard, little   *Otis tetrax*
capercaillie   *Tetrao urogallus*
chough, alpine   *Pyrrhocorax graculus*
crane, black-necked   *Grus nigricollis*
crane, demoiselle   *Anthropoïdes virgo*
crossbill, common   *Loxia curvirostra*
crossbill, parrot   *Loxia pytyopsittacus*
crossbill, white-winged   *Loxia leucoptera*
crow, hooded   *Corvus corone*
duck, common eider   *Somateria mollissima*
duck, white-headed   *Oxyura leucocephala*
eagle, imperial   *Aguila heliaca*
falcon, peregrine   *Falco peregrinus*
flamingo, greater   *Phoenicopterus ruber*
gannet   *Sula bassana*
goose, bar-headed   *Anser indicus*
goose, graylag   *Anser anser*
goose, red-breasted   *Branta ruficollis*
grandala   *Grandala coelicolor*
griffon, Himalayan   *Gyps himalayensis*
grosbeak, pine   *Pinicola enucleator*
grouse, black   *Lyrurus tetrix*
guillemot   *Uria aalge*
gull, Audouin's   *Larus audouinii*
gull, brown-headed   *Larus brunnicephalus*
hen, hazel   *Tetrastes bonasia*
ibisbill   *Ibidorhyncha struthersii*
jay, Hume's ground   *Pseudopodoces humilis*

kingfisher, common   *Alcedo atthis*
kittiwake   *Rissa tridactyla*
lark, desert   *Ammomanes deserti*
magpie, azure-winged   *Cyanopica cyanus*
monal, Chinese   *Lophophorus lhuysii*
nuthatch, Corsican   *Sitta whiteheadi*
owl, barn   *Tyto alba*
owl, hawk   *Surnia ulula*
owl, Lapland   *Strix nebulosa*
owl, pygmy   *Glaucidium passerinum*
owl, Tengmalm's   *Aegolius funereus*
owl, snowy   *Nyctea scandiaca*
partridge, Barbary   *Alectoris barbara*
partridge, Tibetan   *Perdrix hodgsoniae*
partridge, snow   *Lerwa lerwa*
pheasant, golden   *Chrysolophus pictus*
plover, sociable   *Chettusia gregaria*
ptarmigan, willow   *Lagopus lagopus*
puffin   *Fratercula arctica*
raven   *Corvus corax*
redpoll   *Acanthis flammea*
robin, European   *Erithacus rubecula*
roller, European   *Coracias garrulus*
serin   *Serinus serinus*
shrike, woodchat   *Lanius senator*
snipe, solitary   *Gallinago solitaria*
snowcock, Tibetan   *Tetraogallus tibetanus*
sparrow, house   *Passer domesticus*
starling, common   *Sturnus vulgaris*
starling, rose-colored   *Sturnus roseus*
stork, white   *Ciconia ciconia*
tern, arctic   *Sterna paradisaea*
tit, blue   *Parus caeruleus*
tragopan, Temminck's   *Tragopan temmincki*
wall creeper   *Tichodroma muraria*
warbler, Rüppell's   *Sylvia rüppelli*
warbler, subalpine   *Sylvia cantillans*
woodpecker, three-toed   *Picoïdes tridactylus*

Fish

bream   *Abramis brama*
cod, Baikal   *Comephorus baicalensis*
John Dory   *Zeus faber*
mullet, red   *Mullus surmuletus*
pike, northern   *Esox lucius*
perch   *Perca fluviatilis*
sturgeon   *Acipenser güldenstädti*
tuna, bluefin   *Thunnus thynnus*

Invertebrates

bee, or honeybee   *Apis mellifera*
butterfly, striped blue crow   *Euploea mulciber*
coral, red   *Corallium rubrum*
silkworm   *Bombyx mori*
sawfly, European spruce   *Gilpinia heryniae*
worm, cabbage   *Ascia rapae*

Amphibians and Reptiles

agamid, Nepalese   *Agama tuberculata*
frog, marsh   *Rana ridibunda*
gecko, or stenodactylus   *Stenodactylus grandiceps*
lizard, eyed   *Lacerta lepida*
snake, Aesculapian   *Elaphe longissima*
viper, painted desert   *Echis coloratus*

EURASIA
A Reference Map of Place Names

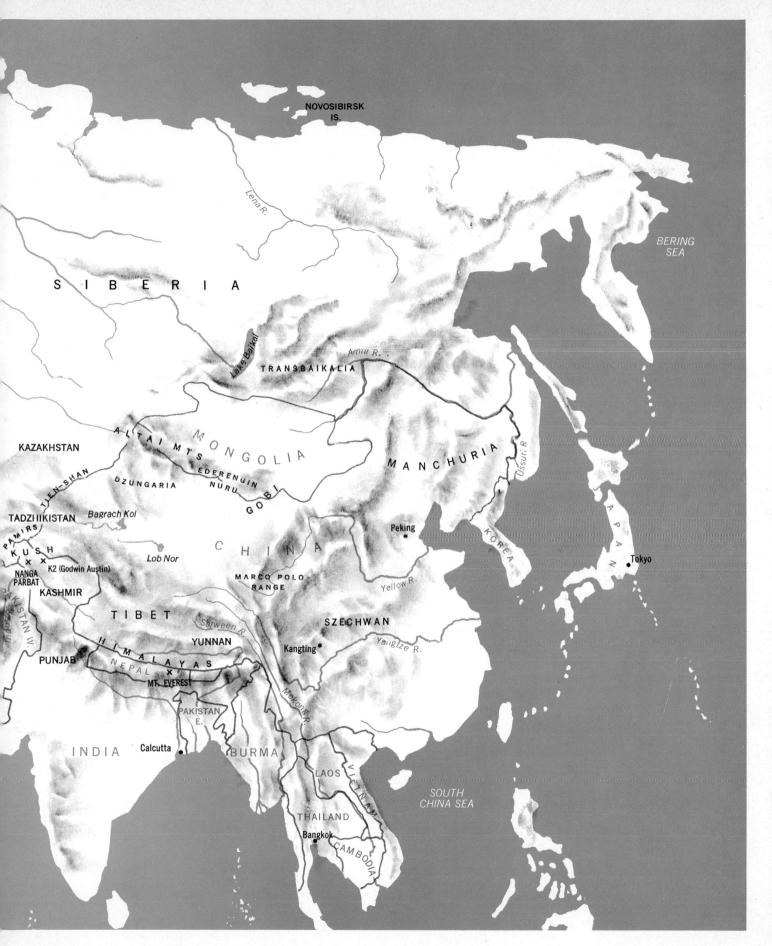

NOVOSIBIRSK
IS.

BERING
SEA

S I B E R I A

TRANSBAIKALIA

Lena R.

Lake Baikal

Amur R.

ALTAI MTS

M O N G O L I A

M A N C H U R I A

Ussuri R.

KAZAKHSTAN

TIEN-SHAN

DZUNGARIA

EDERENGIN
NURU

G O B I

Bagrach Kol

TADZHIKISTAN

PAMIRS

C H I N A

Peking

J A P A N

KOREA

KUSH
× ×
K2 (Godwin Austin)

Lob Nor

NANGA
PARBAT

Tokyo

KASHMIR

MARCO POLO
RANGE

Yellow R.

PAKISTAN W.

T I B E T

Salween R.

SZECHWAN

Yangtze R.

YUNNAN

Kangting

H I M A L A Y A S

PUNJAB

NEPAL
×
MT. EVEREST

Mekong R.

PAKISTAN
E.

INDIA

Calcutta

B U R M A

LAOS

V I E T N A M

SOUTH
CHINA SEA

THAILAND

Bangkok

CAMBODIA

Bibliography

Geography and Regional Descriptions

Berg, L. S., *Natural Regions of the U.S.S.R.* Macmillan, 1950.

Brangham, A. N., *The Naturalist's Riviera*. Phoenix House, 1962.

Darling, F. F., *Natural History in the Highlands and Islands*. Collins, 1947.

Furon, Raymond, *La Paléogéographie*. Payot, 1959.

Harant, H., and D. Jarry, *Guide du Naturaliste dans le Midi de la France* (2 vols.). Delachaux et Niestlé, 1961, 1963.

Hoffman, George W., ed., *A Geography of Europe* (2nd ed.). Ronald, 1961.

Huxley, Julian, *From an Antique Land: Ancient and Modern in the Middle East*. Max Parrish, 1954.

Kachkarov, D. N., and E. P. Korovine, *La Vie dans les Déserts*. French edition by Th. Monod. Payot, 1942.

Kimble, George H. T., and Dorothy Good, *Geography of the Northlands*. The American Geographic Society and John Wiley & Sons, 1955.

Mountfort, Guy, *Portrait of a Wilderness. The Story of the Coto Doñana Expeditions*. Hutchinson, 1958. *Portrait of a River. The Wildlife of the Danube from the Black Sea to Budapest*. Hutchinson, 1962.

Platt, Raye R., *Finland and Its Geography*. Duell, Sloan and Pearce, 1955.

Stamp, L. Dudley, *Asia*. E. P. Dutton, 1962.

Van Valkenburg, Samuel, and Colbert C. Held, *Europe* (2nd ed.). John Wiley & Sons, 1952.

Zenkevitch, I., *Biology of the Seas of the U.S.S.R.* Allen and Unwin, 1963.

Vegetation and Flora

Cooke, Giles B., *Cork and the Cork Tree*. Pergamon Press, 1961.

Cox, E.H.M., *Plant Hunting in China*. Collins, 1945.

Favarger, C., *Flore et Végétation des Alpes* (2 vols.). Delachaux et Niestlé, 1956, 1958.

Giacomini, V., and L. Fenaroli, *Conosci l'Italia* (Vol. II), *La Flora*. Touring Club Italiano, 1958.

Haden-Guest, Stephen, John K. Wright, and Eileen M. Teclaff, eds., *A World Geography of Forest Resources*. Ronald, 1956.

Heim, R., *Les Champignons d'Europe* (2 vols.). Boubée, 1957.

Landolt, E., *Unsere Alpenflora*. Schweizer Alpen-Club, 1960.

McClintock, D., and R.S.R. Fitter, *The Pocket Guide to Wild Flowers*. Collins, 1956.

Pearsall, W. H., *Mountains and Moorlands*. Collins, 1950.

Plant-Water Relationships in Arid and Semi-Arid Conditions. UNESCO, 1960.

Salisbury, Sir Edward, *Weeds & Aliens*. Collins, 1961.

Tansley, A. G., *Britain's Green Mantle: Past, Present, Future*. Allen and Unwin, 1949.

Invertebrate Animals

Barrett, J. H., and C. M. Yonge, *Collins Pocket Guide to the Sea Shore*. Collins, 1958.

Berland, L., *Atlas des Hyménoptères de France, Belgique, Suisse* (2 parts). Boubée, 1958.

Bristowe, W. S., *The World of Spiders*. Collins, 1958.

Clegg, J., *The Freshwater Life of the British Isles*. Warne, 1959.

Corbet, P. S., C. Longfield, and N. W. Moore, *Dragonflies*. Collins, 1960.

Eales, N. B., *The Littoral Fauna of the British Isles* (3rd ed.). Cambridge University Press, 1961.

Ford, E. B., *Butterflies*. Macmillan, 1957. *Moths*. Macmillan, 1955.

Le Cerf, F., and C. Herbulot, *Atlas des Lépidoptères de France, Belgique, Suisse, Italie du Nord* (3 parts). Boubée, 1958-1960.

Luther, W., and K. Fiedler, *Die Unterwasserfauna der Mittelmeerküsten*. Paul Parey, 1961.

Macan, T. T., *A Guide to Freshwater Invertebrate Animals*. Longmans, 1959.

Seguy, E., *Atlas des Diptères de France, Belgique, Suisse* (2 parts). Boubée, 1951.

Utinomi, H., *Coloured Illustrations of Sea Shore Animals of Japan*. Hoikusha, 1960.

Villiers, A., *Atlas des Hémiptères de France* (2 parts). Boubée, 1945, 1947.

Amphibians, Fish and Reptiles

Dottrens, E., *Batraciens et Reptiles d'Europe*. Delachaux et Niestlé, 1963. *Poissons d'Eau Douce* (2 vols.). Delachaux et Niestlé, 1951, 1952.

Jenkins, J. T., *The Fish of the British Isles, Both Freshwater and Salt*. Warne, 1936.

Kamohara, T., *Coloured Illustrations of the Fishes of Japan* (2 vols.). Hoikusha, 1955, 1961.

Smith, M., *The British Amphibians and Reptiles*. Collins, 1951.

Birds

Greenway, James C. Jr., *Extinct and Vanishing Birds of the World*. American Committee for International Wild Life Protection, 1958.

Hollom, P.A.D., *The Popular Handbook of British Birds*. Witherby, 1962. *The Popular Handbook of Rarer British Birds*. Witherby, 1960.

Kobayashi, K., *Birds of Japan in Natural Colours*. Hoikusha, 1956.

Peterson, Roger Tory, G. Mountfort, and P.A.D. Hollom, *A Field Guide to the Birds of Britain and Europe*. Houghton Mifflin, 1954.

Vaurie, Charles, *The Birds of the Palearctic Fauna* (2 vols.). Witherby, 1959, 1964.

Voous, K. H., *Atlas of European Birds*. Nelson, 1960.

Whistler, Hugh, *Popular Handbook of Indian Birds* (4th ed.). Gurney and Jackson, 1949.

Witherby, H. F., ed., *The Handbook of British Birds* (5 vols.). Witherby, 1943.

Yamashina, Y., *Birds in Japan, a Field Guide*. Tokyo News Service, 1961.

Mammals

Hainard, Robert, *Mammifères Sauvages d'Europe* (2 vols., 2nd ed.). Delachaux et Niestlé, 1961, 1962.

Harper, Francis, *Extinct and Vanishing Mammals of the Old World*. American Committee for International Wild Life Protection, 1945.

Imaizumi, Y., *Coloured Illustrations of the Mammals of Japan*. Hoikusha, 1960.

Matthews, L. H., *British Mammals*. Collins, 1952.

Ognev, S. I., *Mammals of the U.S.S.R. and Adjacent Countries* (Vols. I-VI). Israel Program for Scientific Translations, 1963.

Street, Phillip, *Vanishing Animals*. E. P. Dutton, 1961.

Tate, George H. H., *Mammals of Eastern Asia*. Macmillan, 1947.

Van den Brink, F. H., *Die Saugetiere Europas, Westlich des 30 Langengrades*. Paul Parey, 1957.

Human Influences

Dale, Tom, and Vernon Gill Carter, *Topsoil and Civilization*. University of Oklahoma Press, 1955.

Dasmann, Raymond F., *Environmental Conservation*. John Wiley & Sons, 1959.

Stamp, L. Dudley, ed., *A History of Land Use in Arid Regions*. UNESCO, 1961.

Thomas, William L., ed., *Man's Role in Changing the Face of the Earth*. University of Chicago Press, 1956.

Zeuner, Frederick E., *A History of Domesticated Animals*. Hutchinson, 1962.

Miscellaneous

Abrahams, Harold M., ed., *Britain's National Parks*. Country Life, 1959.

Bisch, Jorgen, *Mongolia, Unknown Land*. E. P. Dutton, 1963.

Buck, John Lossing, *Land Utilization in China*. University of Chicago Press, 1937.

Engelhardt, Wolfgang, ed., *Survival of the Free*. G. P. Putnam's Sons, 1962.

Maxwell, Robert, ed., *Information U.S.S.R.* Macmillan, 1962.

McGovern, William Montgomery, *The Early Empires of Central Asia*. University of North Carolina Press, 1939.

National Parks Association of Japan, *National Parks of Japan*. Tokyo News Service, 1957.

United Nations List of National Parks and Equivalent Reserves. International Union for Conservation of Nature and Natural Resources, Part I, 1961; Part II, 1962.

Index

Numerals in italics indicate a photograph or painting of the subject mentioned.